Key to Symbols

Zodiac

♈ Aries

♉ Taurus

♊ Gemini

♋ Cancer

♌ Leo

♍ Virgo

♎ Libra

♏ Scorpio

♐ Sagittarius

♑ Capricorn

♒ Aquarius

♓ Pisces

Recipes

See the "Simpler's Method" article.

〰 Parts by Volume

⚖ Parts by Weight

Moon Phases

● New Moon

◐ First Quarter

○ Full Moon

◑ Last/3rd Quarter

Celestial Symbols

Apogee -The Moon is farthest from the Earth in its orbit.

Perigee -The Moon is closest to the Earth in its orbit.

☍ Opposition -Two celestial bodies appear opposite each other such as the Sun and Moon during a Full Moon. ☉☍☽=○

☌ Conjunction -Two celestial bodies appear together such as the Sun and Moon during a New Moon. ☉☌☽=●

Peak Meteor Shower Days ☽ Moon ♄ Saturn

☿ Mercury ☉ and ☀ Sun ℞ Retrograde

2021 Overview

January

M	T	W	T	F	S	S
				1	2	3
4	5	6	7	8	9	10
11	●12	13	14	15	16	17
18	19	20	21	22	23	24
25	26	27	○28	29	30	31

February

M	T	W	T	F	S	S
1	▢2	◇3	4	5	6	7
8	9	10	●11	12	13	14
15	16	17	18	19	20	21
22	23	24	25	26	○27	28

May

M	T	W	T	F	S	S
				▢1	2	
3	4	◇5	6	7	8	9
10	●11	12	13	14	15	16
17	18	19	20	21	22	23
24	25	○26	27	28	29	30
31						

June

M	T	W	T	F	S	S
	1	2	3	4	5	6
7	8	9	●10	11	12	13
14	15	16	17	18	19	▢20
21	22	23	○24	25	26	27
28	29	30				

September

M	T	W	T	F	S	S
		1	2	3	4	5
●6	7	8	9	10	11	12
13	14	15	16	17	18	19
●20	21	▢22	23	24	25	26
27	28	29	30			

October

M	T	W	T	F	S	S
				1	2	3
4	5	●6	7	8	9	10
11	12	13	14	15	16	17
18	19	●20	21	22	23	24
25	26	27	28	29	30	▢31

Overview Symbols: ● New Moon   ○ Full Moon

Capricorn
Dec 21, 2020 - Jan 19, 2021
Dec 21, 2021, 9:59 am - Jan 2022

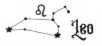

Aquarius
Jan 19, 2:40 pm - Feb 18

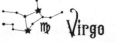

Pisces
Feb 18, 4:44 am - Mar 20

Cancer
Jun 20, 10:32 pm - Jul 22

Leo
Jul 22, 9:27 am - Aug 22

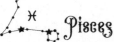

Virgo
Aug 22, 4:35 pm - Sep 22

2021 Overview

March

M	T	W	T	F	S	S
1	2	3	4	5	6	7
8	9	10	11	12	**13**	14
15	16	17	18	19	20	21
22	23	24	25	26	27	28
29	30	31				

April

M	T	W	T	F	S	S
			1	2	3	4
5	6	7	8	9	10	**11**
12	13	14	15	16	17	18
19	20	21	22	23	24	25
26	27	28	29	30		

July

M	T	W	T	F	S	S
			1	2	3	4
5	6	7	8	**9**	10	11
12	13	14	15	16	17	18
19	20	21	22	23	24	25
26	27	28	29	30	31	

August

M	T	W	T	F	S	S
						1
2	3	4	5	6	7	**8**
9	10	11	12	13	14	15
16	17	18	19	20	21	22
23	24	25	26	27	28	29
30	31					

November

M	T	W	T	F	S	S
1	2	3	**4**	5	6	7
8	9	10	11	12	13	14
15	16	17	18	19	20	21
22	23	24	25	26	27	28
29	30					

December

M	T	W	T	F	S	S
		1	2	3	**4**	5
6	7	8	9	10	11	12
13	14	15	16	17	18	19
20	21	22	23	24	25	26
27	28	29	30	31		

▢ Traditional Sabbat   ◇ Exact Cross-Quarter Sabbat

♈ **Aries**
Mar 20, 4:38 am - Apr 19

♉ **Taurus**
Apr 19, 3:34 pm - May 20

♊ **Gemini**
May 20, 2:38 pm - Jun 20

♎ **Libra**
Sep 22, 2:21 pm - Oct 22

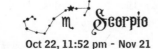
♏ **Scorpio**
Oct 22, 11:52 pm - Nov 21

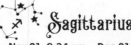
♐ **Sagittarius**
Nov 21, 8:34 pm - Dec 21

Table of Contents

Table of Contents

Using Your Almanac

Planner Pages

Planner Pages begin on page 16. The **right side** of these pages shows the calendar for the week. At the top of each week is a psychic insight and a color. The color can be used to harmonize with that week's energy or as a study queue for color magic.

All astronomical events indicated can be seen with the naked eye or simple binoculars. Viewing and experiencing these events deepens your understanding of both astronomy and astrology. On the **left side** you'll find articles, spells, or recipes that complement the energy of each week. These features are designed to be used as long-term reference material for many years to come.

You'll love having a planner for your schedule that includes notations for traditional Sabbats, lunar phases, meteor showers, eclipses, moon signs, holidays from around the world, seasonal festivals trivia, and other interesting tidbits.

Monthly Overview

In the Planner Pages section a two-page Monthly Overview appears just before the 1st of each month. On the left, you'll find information about that month, bits of trivia, and notable events. On the right is a worksheet showing the month at a glance with the moon phase next to each date. You can use the worksheet to record personal cycles and chart your goals to help you work harmoniously with lunar energies.

Study Guides

Your Monthly Overview includes a handy study guide. Each month a selection of herbs, tarot cards, deities, and exercises are provided to motivate your studies. This is is a flexible learning system that allows you to develop your skills in a wide variety of disciplines whether you are a beginner or have been practicing for decades. Your current level of proficiency, available time, and amount of interest will dictate how intensely you delve into each area. A beginner might simply memorize a single keyword for each of the tarot cards or one magical use for each of the herbs. An advanced practitioner might choose to meditate

for several days on each tarot card, create a bind rune, or culti-
vate some of the herbs.

The link at the bottom of each Study Guide will lead you to
the companion website where you can find more information
about each of the prompts, links for further research, and recommended reading. This link becomes active a few days before the
month begins and remains active until the year 2022. Covens with
outer-court training and solitary beginners may wish to use the
study guides to assist with the traditional year-and-a-day of training prior to dedication or initiation. Seasoned Witches may enjoy
using the guides to rekindle that inner magical fire.

Almanac Time

Your almanac is uniquely suited to help you view astronomical occurrences, plan energy and magical work according to Moon
phases, coordinate rituals to coincide precisely with Sabbats, and
to anticipate astrological events. This is due to the consistent use of
a single time zone used for all data, **Central Time**.

Daylight Savings Time (DST) is already accounted for in the
U.S. and is incorporated into the data so you do not need to add an
hour from March 14 to November 7.

The data for almanacs is "fitted" to a specific place, meaning
that all calculations are based on one location. Usually, this is the
Royal Observatory in Greenwich (GMT) and all data is simply calculated with an hourly offset such as subtracting six hours to get
Central Time. The Practical Witch's Almanac is set for Central
Time and is fitted to W 93° 21', N 34° 35' as indicated by the pin on
the map on the next page[1]. Central Time is easier to convert to
most time zones in North and South America than GMT, and it
covers a large area of the United States, Canada, and Mexico.

**Converting to additional time zones is easy with
the conversions chart and map on the following pages.**

**You can also use the online tools at
PracticalWitch.com/time**

*You can now find Directories of Magical Correspondences for crystals, stones,
colors, candles, herbs, oils, metals, tarot, runes, and days of the week
on the website to further your studies and assist your spellwork.*

Time Zone Conversions

If the map on the opposite page does not show your area, you can go to the PracticalWitch.com website to convert any time, or to look up your "offset". Below is a list of common offsets for major areas. Add or subtract as indicated based on the city that shares your time zone.

Auckland, New Zealand +19	Amsterdam, Netherlands +7
New Plymouth, New Zealand +19	Madrid, Spain +7
Sydney, Australia +17	Rome, Italy +7
Melbourne, Australia +17	Dublin, Ireland +6
Cairns, Australia +16	Lisbon, Portugal +6
Adelaide, Australia +16.5	Prague, Czech Republic +6
Alice Springs, Australia +15.5	Reykjavik, Iceland +6
Tokyo, Japan +15	Glasgow, United Kingdom +6
Perth, Australia +14	Ittoqqortoormiit, Greenland +5
Shanghai, China +14	Nuuk, Greenland +3
Hong Kong, Hong Kong +14	Halifax, Canada +2
New Delhi, India +11.5	Bridgetown, Barbados +2
Moscow, Russia +9	Nassau, Bahamas +1
Cairo, Egypt +8	Ottawa, Canada +1
Athens, Greece +8	Port-au-Prince, Haiti +1
Rovaniemi, Finland +8	New York, NY, USA +1
Paris, France +7	Denver, CO, USA -1
Longyearbyen, Norway +7	Portland, OR, USA -2
Zürich, Switzerland +7	Phoenix, AZ, USA -1 *
Berlin, Germany +7	Honolulu, HI, USA -4

* Most of Arizona does not observe DST except the Navajo Nation and North-East corner of the state). Subtract an extra hour from Almanac Time from Mar. 14 to Nov. 7.

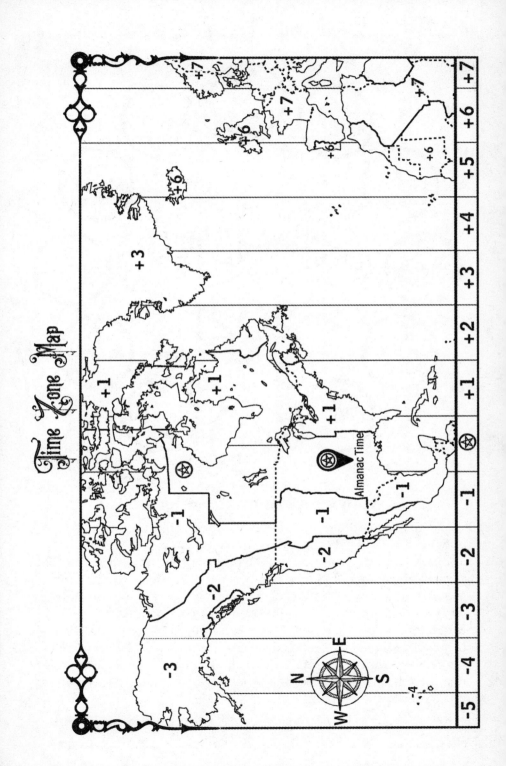

Jan. 12
11:00 pm

Feb. 11
1:05 pm

Dec. 4
1:43 am

Mar. 13
4:21 am

Nov. 4
4:14 pm

New Moons

Apr. 11
9:30 pm

Oct. 6
6:05 am

2021

May 11
1:59 pm

Sep. 6
7:51 pm

Aug. 8
8:49 am

July 9
8:16 pm

June 10
5:52 am

Apogee, Perigee & Supermoons

The Moon at perigee is closest to the Earth in its orbit. At apogee, it is the farthest distance from the Earth. At perigee, it appears 14% larger and up to 30% brighter than at apogee. A Super Full Moon happens when perigee coincides with the Full Moon, and a Super New Moon happens when perigee coincides with the New Moon. The term used for these events at apogee is Micro, giving us Micro Full Moons and Micro New Moons. The Moon at perigee influences oceanic tides (they may be up to 30% higher) and may affect magical workings and wortcunning. Due to atmospheric distortions, the Moon always appears larger when it is closer to the horizon.

Trivia: The best Moon viewing is about an hour after it rises or an hour before it sets.

♌ Jan. 28 1:16 pm

♍ Feb. 27 2:17 am

♈ Mar. 28 1:48 pm

♏ Apr. 26 10:31 pm

♐ May 26 6:13 am

♑ June 24 1:39 pm

♒ July 23 9:36 pm

♒ Aug. 22 7:01 am

♓ Sep. 20 6:54 pm

♈ Oct. 20 9:56 am

♉ Nov. 19 2:57 am

♊ Dec. 18 10:35 pm

Full Moons 2021

Supermoons & Micromoons of 2021

○ Super Full in ♏ & ◐ Partial Lunar Eclipse: April 26, 10:31 pm
● Micro New Moon in ♉: May 11, 1:59 pm
○ Blue Full Moon in ♒ August 22, 7:01 am
● Super New Moon in ♏: November 4, 4:14 pm
○ Micro Full in ♉ & ◐ Partial Lunar Eclipse: Nov. 19, 2:57 am
● Super New Moon in ♐: December 4, 1:43 am
○ Micro Full Moon in ♊: December 18, 10:35 pm

Trivia: A full "Lunar Month" of 24 to 28 days
is called an anomalistic month. A Solar Eclipse always happens within
a couple of weeks of a Lunar Eclipse. See pages 152 and 153.

January Overview

January is National Blood Donor Month
National Braille Literacy Month
National Hobby Month
Hot Tea Month.

Study Guide

Runes: ᚠ Fehu, ᚢ Uruz

Tarot: *Major Arcana:* Fool, Magician *Minor Arcana:* Ace of Wands, Ace of Cups, Ace of Pentacles, Two of Swords

Botanicals: Sage, Frankincense, Ginger, Chives, Wormwood

Crystals & Stones: Aventurine, Quartz Crystal, Citrine, Unakite

Deities: Freya, Tithonus, Yemaya, Bast, Dôn, Shiva, Morrígan

Exercise: Sit or lie down with your back straight. Inhale through your nose to the count of four. Hold for another count of four and then exhale through your mouth to the count of four. Wait four more seconds and then repeat, inhale 4, hold 4, exhale 4, hold 4, etc. Try practicing this *box breathing* technique for five minutes every day.

Welcome to 2021

⊛ The United Nations declared 2021 as the International Year of Peace and Trust, the International Year of Fruits and Vegetables, and the International Year of Creative Economy for Sustainable Development.

⊛ At under fifteen minutes, the shortest total Lunar Eclipse of the 21st Century occurs on May 26th.

⊛ The Great Eastern Brood of cicadas will emerge from the ground in their 17-year cycle. See the Brood X article on page 58.

More Information:
PracticalWitch.com/January

Crafting Your Magic

January

- ○ 1
- ○ 2
- ◔ 3
- ◑ 4
- ◑ 5
- ◑ 6 Last Quarter
- ◑ 7
- ◕ 8
- ◕ 9
- ● 10
- ● 11
- ● 12 New
- ● 13
- ● 14
- ◐ 15
- ◐ 16
- ◐ 17
- ◐ 18
- ◐ 19
- ◐ 20 First Quarter
- ◐ 21
- ◑ 22
- ○ 23
- ○ 24
- ○ 25
- ○ 26
- ○ 27
- ○ 28 Full
- ◑ 29
- ○ 30
- ◑ 31

Almanac Symbols Tutorial

This is the first week of your **Planner Pages** and is a quick walk-through to show you how to read your almanac's symbols. Use the **Key to Symbols** on the inside front cover to find each symbol's meaning. Sabbat symbols can be found on the Wheel opposite of the Key.

Monday the 28th of December on the next page shows ☽Ⅱ. Using the Key, you will note that Ⅱ is the symbol for the astrological sign Gemini and ☽ represents the Moon. This indicates that the Moon is in Gemini on the 28th.

Tuesday the 29th the Moon moves into the Zodiac sign Cancer[2] ☽→♋ at 4:29 am. The Full Moon occurs at 9:28 pm CST and is represented by ○ as indicated in the Key. This Full Moon is in Cancer ♋ as you know because it moved into that sign early Tuesday morning.

Wednesday the 30th the Moon is still in Cancer since Tuesday.

Thursday the 31st begins with the Moon still in Cancer but, at 12:58 pm it enters Leo ☽→♌. Gardeners will be interested in the last notation on the 31st indicating that the planet Saturn ♄ is opposite to the Moon (referred to as "*in opposition*"). This is generally a good time to plant seeds and to use mycorrhizal spores or beneficial nematodes in the garden. Biodynamic gardeners use certain sprays at this time to increase the beneficial microbial activity in the soil.

Friday the 1st the Moon is still in Leo, and you'll see some events, holidays and trivia first of the year. A "Federal" holiday means that U.S. banks, post offices, and government buildings will be closed that day.

Saturday the 2nd the Moon enters Virgo ☽→♍ at 7:13 pm. You will see from the meteor shower symbol ☄ that this is a good night to view shooting stars. The name of the meteor shower follows the symbol, in this case Quadrantids. On page 116, you'll find information about all of this year's meteor showers.

Sunday the 3rd the moon is still in Virgo ☽♍, and the Quadrantids continue their peak nightly show of the year.

Keys symbolize opening opportunities, removing obstacles, unlocking secrets and mysteries, protection, and certain deities such as Hecate.

Take time to look within to discover your true goals, make plans for the year ahead. Color: Lavender

Monday December 28, 2020

☽ ♊

Tuesday 29

☽→♋ 4:29 am
○♋ 9:28 pm

Wednesday 30

Thursday 31

☽ ☍ ♄
☽→♌ 12:58 pm

Friday January 1, 2021

National Hangover Day
New Year's Day (U.S. Federal Holiday)
Sir James George Frazer's Birthday
It is folk custom to we eat beans today for prosperity throughout the year.

Saturday 2

☽→♍ 7:13 pm
Quadrantids

Sunday 3

Quadrantids

Trivia

✸ Altars and fetishes dedicated to Hecate in her triple form were once placed at crossroads. This led her to be identified with the Roman Goddess Trivia, whose name means "triple way" or "of the three ways". The earliest epithet of the Goddess Diana was Trivia.

✸ Google.com has easter eggs (secrets hidden by the coders for fun). Type *askew* into the search box to see one. Try *do a barrel roll* for a fun time, or *recursion* (it will ask if you meant *recursion* and when clicked leads back around), *wizard of oz* (when the knowledge panel comes up, click on the ruby slippers), *metronome* is handy, and for fans of the show Rick & Morty, type in *wubba lubba dub dub* to get an interesting "Did you mean:" suggestion. Douglas Adams fans will find *the answer to life the universe and everything*.

✸ Flax is the plant that gives us linen and its oil is traditionally used to finish wood runes.

✸ The Goddess Arianrhod's name means silver wheel.

✸ Hazelnuts were once more commonly known as filberts.

✸ The word **rede** is very old and its roots in Latin, Old English, Proto-Germanic, Old Frisian, Dutch, and Old Norse all indicate that it means counsel, advice, or help. The Wiccan Rede is the most well-known use of the word, and Wiccans use the Rede to help when making decisions. It is a bit of counsel, not a commandment. The Wiccan Rede has many variations, but a popular version is: *"An it harm none do what ye will"*.

✸ A woodwose is like a satyr or a faun creature often depicted in paintings. It is better known as the "Wildman of the Woods".

✸ Glycerin is a humectant that makes bubbles last longer by drawing moisture from the air. Refill your bottle of bubbles with ¼ cup liquid dish soap, 1 cup water, and 1 teaspoon glycerin (available at most pharmacies). Corn syrup is also a humectant and you can substitute 1 tablespoon corn syrup for the glycerin. You may need to add more than ¼ cup detergent, but start with this recipe and add more if it seems necessary.
Honey is another humectant, but one that is best left out of bubble solutions.

Messages & New Ideas
Color: Red

Monday 4

Trivia Day
☽→♎ 11:42 pm

Tuesday 5

Whip Cream Day

Wednesday 6

◑ 3:37 am
Bean Day

Thursday 7

☽→♏ 2:54 am
International Programmers Day (see also Sept. 13)
Galileo discovers four of Jupiter's moons in 1610

Friday 8

Bubble Bath Day

Saturday 9

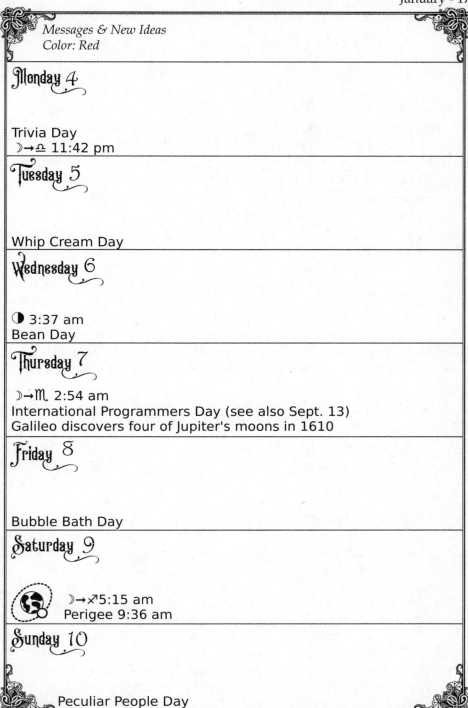

☽→♐ 5:15 am
Perigee 9:36 am

Sunday 10

Peculiar People Day

Ready-Made Herbal Tea Magic

This practical technique is a great way to celebrate Hot Tea Month in January or Hot Tea Day on the 12th while honing your wortcunning skills. Take a close look at the ingredients in your favorite pre-packaged herbal tea or tisane. Research the magical and metaphysical properties of each ingredient to determine what types of spells for which it might be useful.

Celestial Seasonings brand teas are widely available in stores and online. Their *Country Peach Passion*™[3] tea is a great candidate to use as an example. The ingredients (other than natural flavors) are: Orange Peel, Rosehips, Hawthorn, Chamomile, Blackberry Leaves, Hibiscus, Peaches, Paprika. Most of these ingredients correspond to love and divination, but many are also associated with purification and protection. You might share a cup of this tea with a loved one, or drink it while doing tarot readings about relationships. The purification and protection properties can be utilized by making it into an infusion for sprinkling from an aspergillum around your home, or as a wash for scrying crystals and mirrors.

Lemon Kiss Tea

4 Parts Lemon Verbena

1 Part Lemon Balm

2 Parts Red Clover

2 Parts Chamomile

This is a delightful tea that is just as good iced as it is hot. The Simpler's Method on page 20 will give you details about the "parts" if you are not already familiar with apothecary-style recipes. You may simply use handfuls as your "parts" for this recipe. The herbs such as lemon verbena and lemon balm are lightly crushed leaves that have been removed from the stems and dried. The red clover and chamomile are the dried flowers of the plants with no leaves. Combine all ingredients and brew in very hot water (210°F) at a rate of 1 tsp. for every 6 to 8 oz. water.

Express yourself & move on.
Color: Yellow

Monday 11

☽→♑ 7:30 am
Coming of Age Day (Japan)

Tuesday 12

●♑ 11:00 pm
National Hot Tea Day

Wednesday 13

☽→♒ 10:44 am

Thursday 14

Friday 15

National Hat Day
☽→♓ 4:17 pm

Saturday 16

Appreciate a Dragon Day

Sunday 17

The Simpler's Method

Blessing Incense

3 Parts Sandalwood Powder

1 Parts White Copal Powder

1 Parts Ground Cinnamon

1 Part Gum Mastic (optional)

Instructions: On the Full Moon, combine all ingredients using deosil movements.

Apothecary style recipes are provided throughout your almanac. This style of recipes uses the traditional "simpler's method" that gives you the flexibility of "parts". A part can be a measurement of weight or volume. At the beginning of a recipe, you will see a puzzle piece with **waves to indicate that the recipe's parts are by volume**, or a **scale to indicate parts by weight.**

Recipe Symbols

Parts by Volume

For the blessing incense above, the puzzle piece at the top indicates volume. If you wish to make a small amount, you could use a teaspoon (tsp.) as each part. You would then use 3 tsp. sandalwood, 1 tsp. copal and 1 tsp. cinnamon. For a large batch, you might use a tablespoon instead of a teaspoon.

Parts by Weight

If this blessing incense recipe had been *parts by weight* (with a scale puzzle piece) you can change the amount you are making simply by changing the part size. For example, you can make a tiny batch of a recipe with parts by weight using grams as your part, or a larger batch using ounces.

Trivia: The dot over an i or j is called a tittle.

Conflict resolved, compromises
Color: Gold

Monday 18

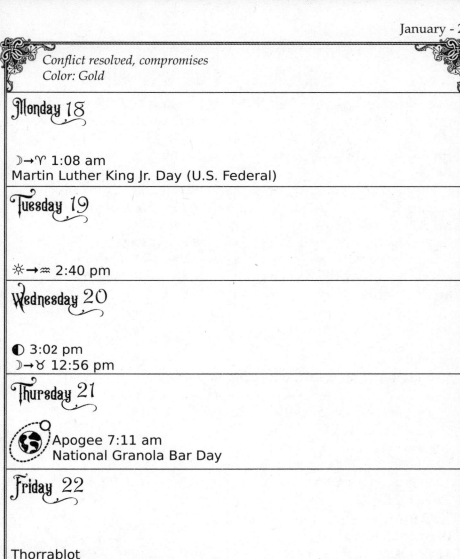

☽→♈ 1:08 am
Martin Luther King Jr. Day (U.S. Federal)

Tuesday 19

☀→♒ 2:40 pm

Wednesday 20

☽ 3:02 pm
☽→♉ 12:56 pm

Thursday 21

Apogee 7:11 am
National Granola Bar Day

Friday 22

Thorrablot

Saturday 23

☽→♊ 1:43 am

Sunday 24

Compliment Day
View Mercury low on the western horizon just after sunset

Crafting the Cakes & Ale

These cakes can be the other half of "cakes and ale" especially if your "ale" is milk! They are nearly fat-free and can be made vegetarian or even vegan. Use a regular 13 x 9 inch pan, 12-hole muffin tin, or two jelly roll pans. Spray your choice of pan heavily with non-stick spray or use traditional grease and flour.

When you use jelly-roll pans you can cut out shapes with cookie cutters. Do this at the last minute because they dry out quickly without frosting. You can put the shapes on a rack and drizzle them with melted chocolate instead of frosting. Try sprinkling powdered sugar from a sifter over the cake. For fun designs, cover the cake with a lace doily, or use a stencil to make interesting sugar designs appropriate to your Sabbat.

Sabbat Cakes

In a big bowl or cauldron mix the following:
1 cup cool strong coffee...cola or root beer work too
½ teaspoon lemon juice or vinegar
½ teaspoon cloves
1 teaspoon cinnamon
2 teaspoons vanilla extract
1 tablespoon cornstarch, arrowroot powder, or rice flour
1 egg (optional)
Add the following atop the liquid and then mix thoroughly.
1 ½ cups unbleached flour
½ teaspoon sea salt or salt (optional)
½ cup cocoa
1 teaspoon baking soda
1 cup sugar

Pour into pan(s) and bake at **350°F** until a toothpick inserted into the center comes out clean. For 13 x 9 inch pans this is about 35 minutes. Muffin tins about 15-20 minutes. Jelly-roll pans about 10-15 minutes. Cool completely before frosting, or you can sprinkle with powdered sugar or drizzle with chocolate.

Seek wise counsel. Color: Aqua | Trivia: Lunacy was thought to be a disorder caused by the Moon in the 16th century.

Monday 25

☽→♋ 12:52 pm
Opposite Day

Tuesday 26

Australia Day
Republic Day (India)

Wednesday 27

☽→♌ 8:54 pm
National Chocolate Cake day

Thursday 28

○♌ 1:16 pm

Friday 29

Saturday 30

☿ ℞ 9:51 am
☽→♍ 2:03 am
National Seed Swap Day

Sunday 31

February Overview

February is Black History Month (U.S. & Canada) LGBTQIA+ History Month (UK), American Heart Month, and Great American Pie Month.

Study Guide

Runes: ᚦ Thurisaz, ᚨ Ansuz

Tarot: *Major Arcana:* High Priestess, Empress *Minor Arcana:* Two of Wands, Two of Cups, Two of Pentacles, Two of Swords

Botanicals: Rosemary, Cinnamon, Vervain, Catnip, Eucalyptus

Crystals & Stones: Rose Quartz, Garnet, Jasper, Rhodonite

Deities: Loki, Phobetor, Mórrígan, Brigit (Brigid), Babalú Ayé, Mokosh (Mokoš)

Exercise: In this exercise, you will be visualizing a single color field. Close your eyes and try to visualize just the color red filling all of your inner vision. Think about red and "see" red. This may take some time, but be patient and keep working at it. Try this several times throughout the day and especially before bed until you can easily accomplish this single color visualization.

If you find it difficult to do this visualization, don't get frustrated. Each time you attempt this exercise, you are developing important visualization skills. One day you will find that it is so simple for you to accomplish this visualization, that you'll wonder why you ever found it challenging.

Try different colors: Red, Orange, Yellow, Green, Blue, Indigo, Violet. You may find it easier one color easier than others. You may also discover it is easier for you to do this visualization at certain times of the day or night, during different moon phases, or different personal moods.

More Information: PracticalWitch.com/February

February

1
2 ⊕ Sabbat
3 ⊕ Exact Cross-Quarter 8:40 am
4 Last Quarter
5
6
7
8
9
10
11 New
12
13
14
15
16
17
18
19 First Quarter
20
21
22
23
24
25
26
27 Full
28
29
30
31

Imbolc Sabbat
Imbolc /Imbolg/Brigid's Day

On Tuesday of this week, Witches around the world will be celebrating the Sabbat. For those of us in the Northern Hemisphere, we call this Sabbat Imbolc, Imbolg, or Brigid's Day. Witches in the Southern Hemisphere may be celebrating Lughnasadh or Lammas at this time (see page 88).

Imbolc marks the beginning of spring. Like most Sabbats, celebrations begin the night before on the 1st. Fires and candles are lit to represent the returning sun, and symbols of fertility adorn many altars. Colcannon or mashies are traditional dishes, and an overall sense of "spring fever" crackles in the air. Weaving Brigid's Crosses such as the one pictured is a favorite way to celebrate. These equal-armed crosses are hung over doorways and windows for protection and to welcome Brigid.

The Southern Hemisphere Witch

The inside covers of your Almanac have a Wheel of the Year with all of this year's Sabbats and Esbats. The name of the Sabbat you celebrate on the dates indicated depends on your **tradition** and **location**. You can customize the Wheel on page 156.

Witches in the Southern Hemisphere (SH) sometimes follow the traditional Northern Hemisphere (NH) Sabbats, celebrating Samhain in October as do most UK and U.S. traditions. However, it can be difficult to prepare for this harvest Sabbat when it is early spring outside your door. The season in the SH in October is that of Beltane in the NH. For some SH Witches, it makes sense to work harmoniously with the cycles of nature, celebrating the Sabbats according to the current local season. Many SH initiates will begin their practice by following the NH Wheel because that is what their traditions and books teach but, often change to the SH Wheel once they move from studying into practice. For these SH Witches, Sabbats are on the opposite sides of the Wheel just like the hemispheres are opposite each other.

NH Imbolc = SH Lughnasadh   NH Ostara = SH Mabon
NH Beltane = SH Samhain   NH Litha = SH Yule

Someone loves you.
Color: Green

Monday 1

☽→♎ 5:26 am
National Freedom Day
Day off for Constitution Day (Mexico)

Tuesday 2

Groundhog Day
Sabbat: Imbolc/Lughnasadh

Wednesday 3

☽→♏ 8:15 am
Perigee 1:02 pm
Cross-Quarter Sabbat 8:40 am (☉ at 15° ♒)

Thursday 4

◑11:37 am
Rosa Parks Day (California & Missouri)

Friday 5

☽→♐ 11:17 am
Constitution Day (Mexico)

Saturday 6

Waitangi Day (New Zealand)

Sunday 7

☽→♑ 2:52 pm
Super Bowl LV (55) Scheduled

Crafting an Elemental Spell

Witches use the classical elements[4] of Earth, Air, Fire, Water in magic. An easy way to begin designing a spell is to choose something associated with your goal that corresponds to each of the elements.  Let's use a prosperity spell as an example. The color green corresponds to growth and prosperity, so you might select a green candle for fire. Aventurine stone is said to draw in opportunities and good fortune, so the stone can represent the earth element. Comfrey is associated with both water and prosperity so you can use it for the water correspondence. Lavender is associated with air and money so you could use lavender incense for your air element. Designing your spell around the elements is an opportunity to let your creativity thrive. One way to cast this spell would be to enter into a relaxed, focused mental state. The breathing exercises from January may help.

Visualize your goal, and imagine that you have already achieved its outcome. Crumble a pinch of comfrey onto the top of a votive candle while saying words of power you've written, or something like *Prosperity flows into my life.* Continue to focus and visualize. Light the candle and saying: *I burn away poverty and strife.* Using the flame of the candle, light the incense while saying: *The winds of change bring luck to me.* Hold the aventurine, continue to focus and visualize and say: *As I will it, so mote it be.*

Pass the stone through the flame of the candle and the smoke of the incense. **The act of infusing something through incense smoke is called censing.** Hold the stone in your hand and focus your energy and visualization. You can repeat the words of power while you do this. Carry the stone with you until the spell's effects are apparent in your life.

The last line of this spell is a traditional Witch's way of sealing a spell and sending its energy out into the world. I've also intentionally used the word "will" in this spell because it has been associated with the element Earth since around the time of the writings of 19th century French occultist Éliphas Lévi. In setting forth his Powers of the Sphinx he states *"Everything is possible to him who wills only what is true! Rest in Nature, study, know, then dare; dare to will, dare to act and be silent!"*. These four powers have been utilized by occultists such as Aleister Crowley and are associated with the four elements:
know=air, **dare**=fire, **will**=earth, **keep silent**=water

Gatherings are discouraged.
  Color: Teal

Monday 8

National Kite Flying Day
Waitangi Day observed (New Zealand)

Tuesday 9

☽→♒ 7:21 pm
National Pizza Day

Wednesday 10

Thursday 11

●♒ 1:05 pm
National Foundation Day (Japan)
Chinese New Year, Year of the metal Ox Begins (Spring Festival)

Friday 12

Lincoln's Birthday
☽→♓ 1:24 am
Carnival Friday (Brazil)

Saturday 13

Lupercalia Begins
Carnival Saturday (Brazil)

Sunday 14

☽→♈ 9:54 am
Valentine's Day
Carnival Sunday (Brazil)

The Witch's Cords

There are many rituals such as handfastings and some initiations[5] that use cords, and knot magic is a handy skill to develop. You might enjoy finding special cords for your altar such as the soft ropes used to tie back curtains, or silk ropes made especially for contact with skin. Tassels have been used for centuries to ward off bad luck and can be added to the ends of your cords for style.

Marking Out a Circle

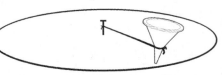

Determine how large of a circle you want and divide the measurement in half. For a 9 foot circle, you need 4 ½ feet of cord. Anchor one end of your cord to the ground where you want the center of your circle. Anchor with a garden stake outdoors, or painter's tape indoors. Tie a large piece of sidewalk chalk to the cord at the length you calculated earlier (4 ½ feet) or tie a funnel to the end. Fill your funnel with a marking material and use your finger to cover the bottom hole to help you regulate the flow of marking material. For outdoor rituals use environmentally safe material in your funnel such as cornmeal. Salt can be used as a marking material indoors, and this salt can be reused many times.

Lunar Knot Magic

As with all ritual and magical tools, your cords become more imbued with energy each time you use them. You can also intentionally charge your cords with lunar energy for later use. This is a helpful technique when the moon is waning but you wish to work with the energy of the Full Moon. Find a place where you have a good view of the Full Moon. Center yourself and enter the meditative state you use to work magic. Hold the cord in front of you while gazing at the moon, drawing the lunar energy into the cord. Tie a knot in the cord and just as you pull it tight, center the image of the Moon inside the knot. When you wish to use the energy of the Full Moon, untie the knot to release it. The colors of your cords can be chosen for their magical purposes, or try white cord for the Full Moon and black cord for the New Moon. When charging cords with the energy of the New Moon, consider working during the day when the moon is overhead and visualize the moon inside the knot.

No News
Color: Gray

Monday 15

Lupercalia Ends
Carnival Monday (Brazil)
Susan B. Anthony's Birthday
President's Day (U.S. Federal)

Tuesday 16

)→♉ 9:12 pm
Shrove Tuesday/Mardi Gras
Carnival Tuesday (Brazil)

Wednesday 17

Chinese New Year Holiday Ends
Carnival ends at 2pm in Brazil

Thursday 18

⊙→♓ 4:44 am
Apogee 4:21 am

Friday 19

◖12:47 pm
)→♊ 10:04 am

Saturday 20

☿ Direct 6:45 pm
World Day of Social Justice

Sunday 21

)→♋ 9:53 pm
Barbara Jordan's Birthday

Crafting Your Spells: Law of Similarity

Sympathetic magic is used to some degree in every faith and culture worldwide. Throughout history, people have built a variety of techniques based on two main principles of how sympathetic magic works. Similar to the laws of physics, these principles are regarded as the basic foundation on which we build our spells. Once you understand these two principles, you can craft your style of magic that resonates with you better than spells created by others. The first principle is the *Law of Similarities* below, and the second is the *Law of Contagion* covered on page 36.

This is the principle of "like attracts like". Similarities can be in the form of *imitation* such as a fetish or poppet made to resemble the target of a spell, or a photo being used as a focus for a spell. Similarities may also be drawn through *correspondences*. When we use plants, stones, and other items that are associated with certain traits we are using correspondences. The Doctrine of Signatures was a concept used for centuries to determine the correspondence of an item with a trait. An item such as a walnut looks similar to the human brain. The Doctrine of Signatures tells us that walnuts then must be good for the brain. This doctrine assumed that Mother Nature labeled items for our use. The practice has been surprisingly successful, leading us to use foxglove's heart-shaped leaves to indicate its usefulness for the heart. To this day, digitalis (a primary chemical found in foxglove) is used as a heart medicine. The practice was fraught with the potential for error and has been abandoned in modern medicine and herbalism while remaining influential in magic.

Often a correspondence of a trait with a color, herb, or crystal will develop through repeated use by a culture. The color green is associated with growth. In Western occultism, it is also associated with money. We see the lush green abundance of the forests and grasslands and associate the color with growth, and U.S. dollars are green in color. However, in China and Japan, red is associated with abundance and vitality in a way Western occultists associate the color green. Red envelopes containing money are exchanged at the Chinese New Year.

Trivia: Italian Witches call the evil eye *malocchio*.

Work changes.
Color: Blue

Monday 22

Sybil Leek's Birthday

Tuesday 23

National Dog Biscuit Day
Emperor's Birthday (Japan)

Wednesday 24

☽→♌ 6:23 am

Thursday 25

National Chili Day

Friday 26

☽→♍ 11:07 am
Chinese Lantern Festival

Saturday 27

○♍ 2:17 am
National Retro Day

Sunday 28

☽→ ♎ 1:17 pm
National Tooth Fairy Day

March Overview

March is National Women's History Month, Social Workers Month, National Craft Month, and National Irish American Heritage Month.

Study Guide

Runes: ᚱ Raidho, ᚲ Kenaz

Tarot: *Major Arcana:* Emperor, Hierophant *Minor Arcana:* Three of Wands, Three of Cups, Three of Pentacles, Three of Swords

Botanicals: Sandalwood, Dragon's Blood, Myrrh, Cloves, Jasmine

Crystals & Stones: Obsidian, Tourmaline, Labradorite, Malachite

Deities: Odin, Iah, Sucellos, Baudihillie, Arianrhod, Guanyin

Exercise: In this exercise, you will be visualizing a single, two-dimensional shape of a solid color. Start by picturing a flat, red circle as if it were a sticker on a piece of paper. Try other colors: Red, Orange, Yellow, Green, Blue, Indigo, Violet. Change the shape to a square, then try other more complex shapes.

Trivia: A labyrinth is an ancient device much like a maze, except there is only one path to the center. Large labyrinths can be created out of stepping-stones outdoors and walked as a form of personal meditation. Some people use pictures of labyrinths such as the one here. Trace the path in the labyrinth pictured to travel the same circuitous route pattern used since the Bronze Age.

More Information: PracticalWitch.com/March

March

○ 1
○ 2
○ 3
○ 4
○ 5 Last Quarter
◑ 6
◑ 7
◑ 8
◑ 9
● 10
● 11
● 12
● 13 New
● 14
◐ 15
◐ 16
◐ 17
◐ 18
◐ 19
◐ 20 ✪ Equinox Sabbat 4:37 am
◐ 21 First Quarter
◐ 22
◐ 23
○ 24
○ 25
○ 26
○ 27
○ 28 Full
○ 29
○ 30
○ 31

Crafting Your Spells: Law of Contagion

The Law of Contagion is the second of the two basic principles of sympathetic magic. On page 32 you learned about the Law of Similarity but, the Law of Contagion is perhaps the most akin to modern scientific thought. This is the principle that two things that have been in contact with each other maintain a magical link as the essence of each is imbued into the other. Think of it like the transfer of molecules when two people or things come into contact, or the transfer of fingerprints left on items.

The magical link that remains between two things can only be severed through a cleansing, banishing, or consecration. This is why ritual tools used on the Witch's altar are cleansed and consecrated before their first use. The cleansing severs previous magical links, and the consecration sets the tool aside as dedicated to the Witch's intent to prevent it from becoming re-contaminated.

In sympathetic magical practice, the Law of Contagion is often combined with the Law of Similarity such as with the use of a poppet. A doll might be fashioned to look similar to the target of a spell (Similarity) and then hair from the target might be used as the poppet's hair (Contagion). Pieces of fabric from a target's clothing might be used to make clothes for the poppet, or used as stuffing for the doll. The poppet is now an imitation of the target with corresponding items from the target.

Imagine someone has asked you to send healing energy to them after knee replacement surgery. A poppet such as the one pictured could be stuffed with a mixture of herbs corresponding to healing such as rosemary, lavender, and mint. You could add healing stones such as moss agate and bloodstone. The hair could be donated from the person requesting the healing (the spell's target) and while focusing your intent you can channel healing energy with pinpoint accuracy to send healing energy to the person's knee.

Psychics who practice psychometry are using the Law of Contagion. They tap into the essence left upon objects and places by people and events.

Light at the end of the tunnel.
  Color: Light Blue

Monday 1

Matronalia
Perigee 11:18 pm
Zero Discrimination Day

Tuesday 2

☽→♏ 2:39pm
Read Across America Day
National Academy of Science founded 1863

Wednesday 3

World Wildlife Day

Thursday 4

☽→♐ 4:43 pm

Friday 5

◐7:30 pm
Employee Appreciation Day

Saturday 6

☽→♑ 8:21 pm
☿ low in the eastern horizon just before sunrise.

Sunday 7

National Cereal Day

Friday's Far-Flung Forecasts

　　While creating the insights at the top of each week's planner pages, I try to look ahead at the coming year psychically and astrologically. Of course, the logical reading of patterns plays a huge role in any psychic's efforts. Sometimes there are *flashes* of headlines that come into the mind's eye. Traditionally I leave these out of your almanac because it is difficult to predict so far into the future on a global scale with so many potentialities in play. These predictions are for entertainment only and should not be used for gambling or investment purposes. So for your entertainment…

Ϙ Oscar & Academy Awards take a twist with many awards going to streaming and Video-on-Demand films from services such as Netflix. Flashes of animations coming out of Universal and Warner Brothers, as well as the name Spike Lee.

Ϙ This year's fashion word is **cozy**! Comfortable clothing appears on the haute couture runways as well as prêt-à-porter at the big-box stores.

Ϙ Railways in China and India repeatedly hit the headlines.

Ϙ Housing prices will recover from the 2020 pandemic dip by late 2021.

Ϙ U.S. inflation rises dramatically over the rate of the previous 15 years.

Ϙ Self-driving cars hit headlines in the U.S., China, and the UK.

Ϙ China: Headlines about Artificial Intelligence and robot submarines?

Ϙ The UK moon rover experiences delays, but will send back incredible HD video that may go viral.

Ϙ Roadside saliva drug testing in New Zealand gets a lot of attention.

Ϙ Facial recognition identification becomes standard and all U.S. International airports. By the end of the year it is standard in and around all major federal buildings and large business districts and then quickly drops out of the headlines.

Ϙ Aurora, the first exascale supercomputer in the U.S. will make headlines regularly during its final phases of development and for its calculation results.

Ϙ There is a strong focus on Nationalism in almost every large country in the world. Political extremism continues to rise.

Communication, Travel, Business matters begin to improve this week.
Color: Yellow

Monday 8

International Women's Day

Tuesday 9

☽→♒ 1:41 am

Wednesday 10

Harriet Tubman's Birthday

Thursday 11

☽→♓ 8:44 am
Douglas Adam's Birthday

Friday 12

National Plant a Flower Day

Saturday 13

☽→♈ 5:44 pm
●♓ 4:21 am

Sunday 14

Daylight Saving Time begins at 2:00am
Set Clocks ahead +1 hour (U.S.)
Albert Einstein's Birthday

Pi Day

Ostara Sabbat

Ostara is all about the light of the Sun growing stronger. After this equinox, the days grow longer as life emerges from winter's rest. This is the official first day of spring and we adorn our altars with symbols of fertility, fresh flowers, decorated eggs, and seeds.

Activities include blessing garden seeds, rituals for manifesting goals for the year, music, and dance. Rituals are performed and spells are cast with the themes of new beginnings, new life, and balance.

Foods traditionally served may include eggs, hot cross buns (Witches usually call these Cross-Quarter buns), lamb, sprouts, salads, and dandelions. A great item to bring to pot-luck rituals is deviled eggs garnished with dandelion flowers, calendula petals, chive flowers, or nasturtium blossoms. *If you are celebrating Mabon in the Southern Hemisphere right now, see page 106.*

Egg-Optional Egg Salad

For this recipe, you can choose between using **8-12 boiled and peeled eggs or 2 ½ cups cubed pressed tofu**. To press your tofu, start with 16 to 20 ounces of an extra firm style. Drain any water from the tofu and wrap it in a clean towel. Place the wrapped tofu on a flat plate and put another plate on top of it. Add some weight to the top plate such as a large bowl or canned food item. Allow this to sit in your refrigerator a few hours or overnight. After pressing, gently slice the tofu into ½ inch cubes.

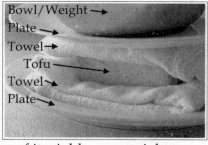

Bowl/Weight →
Plate →
Towel →
Tofu →
Towel →
Plate →

Combine ½ cup mayonnaise, 1 tsp. prepared yellow mustard, ½ cup chopped green onions (or ¼ cup minced chives). Stir in chopped eggs or cubed pressed tofu. Season to taste with salt and pepper. For variations add ⅓ cup finely chopped celery, ¼ cup sweet pickle relish, or 1 tsp. prepared wasabi for a kick.

Skills rewarded.
Color: Palest Sky Blue

Monday 15

Ides of March (Brutus stabs Caesar 44 B.C.E.)
Day off for Benito Juárez's Birthday Memorial (Mexico)

Tuesday 16

 ☽→♉ 5:57 am

Wednesday 17

St. Patrick's Day -He drove the "snakes" (Pagans) out of Ireland

Thursday 18

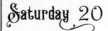 ☽→♊ 6:47 pm
Apogee 12:03 am
National Awkward Moments Day

Friday 19

Saturday 20

International Day of Happiness
See Venus on the eastern horizon before sunrise
Equinox Sabbat: Mabon/Ostara (☉ 0°♈ 4:38 am)

Sunday 21

☽→♋ 7:18 am | ☽ 9:40 am
World Poetry Day | International Day of Forests
Benito Juárez's Birthday Memorial (Mexico)
World Day to Eliminate Racial Discrimination

The Names of the Moons

There are many different names for the same Full Moon in any given month or season. This variety is entirely appropriate, as regional and cultural differences are reflected in the names. Below is a worksheet with historical Moon names listed next to an empty column for you to fill in a name for each month's Moon based on your personal experiences, traditions, and observations. The most common name for a month's Moon is listed first, followed by popular alternates.

Month	Traditional Names	Your Name
Jan.	Wolf Moon, Nursing Moon, Winter Moon, Milk Moon, Cold Moon	
Feb.	Storm or Snow Moon, Horning Moon, Fasting or Hunger Moon, Weaning Moon	
Mar.	Worm Moon, Seed Moon, Chaste Moon, Planter's Moon, Sap Moon	
Apr.	Hare Moon, Mating Moon, Frog Moon, Flower Moon, Seed Moon, Egg Moon	
May	Dyad Moon, Journey Moon, Mead Moon, Strawberry Moon, Rose Moon, Milk Moon	
June	Honey or Mead Moon, Strawberry Moon, Hay Moon, Wort Moon, Mother's Moon	
July	Wort Moon, Hay Moon, Grain Moon, Father's Moon, Barley Moon, Elk Moon	
Aug.	Barley Moon, Nesting Moon, Harvest Moon, Wine Moon, Sturgeon Moon	
Sep.	Harvest Moon, Wine Moon, Barley Moon	
Oct	Blood Moon, Harvest Moon, Hunting Moon, Culling Moon, Pumpkin Moon	
Nov.	Snow Moon, Beaver Moon, Death Moon Oak Moon	
Dec.	Cold Moon, Big Moon, Oak Moon, Long Night's Moon, *Wolf Moon	

* *The Wolf Moon is the first Full Moon after the December Solstice. For most years such as 2021, this Full Moon occurs in January so it begins this list of Moon Names. In 2023, the Wolf Moon will be on December 26th.*

Fears overcome.
Color: Scarlet

Monday 22

World Water Day

Tuesday 23

$)\rightarrow \Omega$ 4:57 pm
Puppy Day

Wednesday 24

National Chocolate Covered Raisin Day

Thursday 25

$)\rightarrow \mathrm{M}$ 10:26 pm
Waffle Day

Friday 26

Dr. Jonas Salk[6]announced his polio vaccine

Saturday 27

Sunday 28

$\bigcirc \simeq$ 1:48 pm
$)\rightarrow \simeq$ 12:23 am
Weed Appreciation Day
Daylight Saving Time begins (in the UK & Germany)

April Overview

April is National Child Abuse Prevention Month, National Poetry Month, National Autism Awareness Month, National Volunteer Month, National Humor Month, and Sexual Assault Awareness Month.

Study Guide

Runes: X Gebo, ᛈ Wunjo

Tarot: *Major Arcana:* Lovers, Chariot *Minor Arcana:* Four of Wands, Four of Cups, Four of Pentacles, Four of Swords

Botanicals: Chamomile, Lemon Balm, Rose, Broom (Broomcorn)

Crystals & Stones: Amazonite, Celestite, Lapis Lazuli, Hematite

Deities: Thor, Hermes, Andraste, Isis, Cáer, Zorya (Zorya Utrennyaya, Zorya Vechernyaya, and Zorya Polunochnaya)

Exercise: Visualize a sphere or ball. This three-dimensional shape exercise is easier if you can find a simple sphere around your home or at a store. Ping-pong balls, gum-ball machine "super" balls, and other smooth spherical objects work well.

Place the ball in front of you on a table or hold it cupped in your hands. Close your eyes and try to visualize the sphere. Open your eyes occasionally to verify the accuracy of your visualization.

Once you can clearly bring the image of the ball into your mind's eye, change its color. Start with red and go through orange, yellow, green, blue, indigo, and violet.

Trivia: Have you ever heard someone say that it is a "red-letter day"? This turn of phrase means that it is an especially good or important day and goes back to a time when calendars had the names of holidays printed in red ink, similar to the bold printing for the Sabbats in the planner pages of your almanac.

More Information: PracticalWitch.com/April

April

1
2
3
4 Last Quarter
5
6
7
8
9
10
11 New
12
13
14
15
16
17
18
19
20 First Quarter
21
22
23
24
25
26 Full
27
28
29
30
31

The Witch's Incense

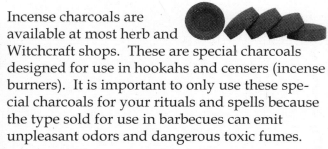

Incense charcoals are available at most herb and Witchcraft shops. These are special charcoals designed for use in hookahs and censers (incense burners). It is important to only use these special charcoals for your rituals and spells because the type sold for use in barbecues can emit unpleasant odors and dangerous toxic fumes.

Incense charcoals usually come in foil-wrapped rolls that should be stored in an airtight container once opened. Self-lighting types contain saltpeter to help them light evenly. This makes a sparkling, crackle effect that is especially lovely in a darkened room or moonlit ritual.

You will need a heat-proof container such as a cauldron or censer. A layer of black sand or gravel on the bottom of your cauldron creates better airflow for the charcoal. This also keeps the cauldron from getting too hot and scorching surfaces or weakening the metal.

To light your charcoal, hold an edge to a flame until the sparkling begins. For aggressively sparkly charcoals, I use antique claw ice tongs to hold the charcoal over a candle and then place it into the cauldron. This keeps small sparks away from hands and clothing and prevents burns.

Wait a few minutes until the charcoal has an even glow. In brightly lit areas where you cannot see the glow of the coal, wait until a layer of ash appears over the charcoal.

Continued on page 48

Care for your heart.
Color: Pink

Monday 29

National Vietnam War Veterans Day

Tuesday 30

 Perigee 1:16 am
)→♏ 12:34 am

Wednesday 31

Thursday 1

April Fool's Day
)→♐ 12:59 am

Friday 2

Good Friday (observed in some states, stock markets closed)

Saturday 3

)→♑ 3:13 am
National Find a Rainbow Day

Sunday 4

◑5:02 am
Maya Angelou's Birthday
Daylight Saving Time ends in Australia | Easter

Continued from page 46

All smoke and sparking should be finished in about five minutes and your charcoal is then ready for use. Place a very small amount of incense on top of the charcoal. You should not cover more than half of the charcoal's top surface. For large charcoals, this is about ½ teaspoon, and for small charcoals about ¼ teaspoon. The incense recipes in your almanac are specifically designed for use on incense charcoals. This type of incense offers considerable advantages. Besides being able to customize your blend for specific energy purposes, you can switch blends at any time.

For example, you might begin your ritual with a circle incense for cleansing and clearing and later switch to a custom blend designed specifically for your working. You can add small pinches of incense as desired for fragrance or as required by your ritual or spell. Charcoals burn an average of 45 minutes, so you have plenty of time to work a full spell.

Resins like frankincense, copal, myrrh, opopanax, mastic, or benzoin will burn for a longer period of time than ground herbs and spices. When using the recipes in your almanac, prepare your ingredients so that they are all about the same size. Resins should be lightly crushed so that all pieces are consistent in size and are about the same size as any crushed leaves and flowers in the blend.

Same State Memory

It is strongly recommended that you consider using the same incense every time you prepare for magical or spiritual work. Through repeated use and association, your mind will enter into a beneficial mind state more quickly with fragrance assisting you. The power of scent is strongly linked to memory, and this simple technique can save you a lot of time.

Try using a sandalwood, nag champa, or circle incense every time you cast a circle, begin meditating, or before you do yoga. This clears and harmonizes the surrounding energies, and triggers your mind to enter into the same relaxed, open state every time. When you use this technique consistently and frequently it will quickly develop into a powerful skill.

Choose your path now.
Color: Orange

Monday 5

☽→♒ 8:04 am
Easter Monday

Tuesday 6

National Tartan Day
National Library Workers' Day

Wednesday 7

☽→♓ 3:31 pm
United Nations World Health Day

Thursday 8

International Romani Day

Friday 9

National Name Yourself Day

Saturday 10

☽→♈ 1:11 am

Sunday 11

●♈ 9:30 pm
National Pet Day

Ready–for–Love Spell

This is a surprisingly powerful self-confidence, beauty, and general attraction spell. It is designed to avoid manipulating others and you can repeat this spell once a week to improve its effects and build your self-esteem. Respecting and honoring yourself is the most powerful way to attract people to you. This spell will help you project your best assets and build your personal magical energy.

You will need:

¼ Cup Sea Salt	3 White or Pink Candles
Towels and/or Sheets	1 Rose Quartz Stone
Access to a Bathroom	Various optional items
Music	*(see directions below)*

Thoroughly clean the bathroom and cover the mirrors with sheets or towels. Arrange and light the candles around the room. Draw your bath water, drop in the rose quartz, and add the salt while saying the words of power italicized below. (If you only have access to a shower, tie the salt up in a washcloth while saying the words of power.) *Negativity is washed away, I am renewed as of today. Many heads will turn my way, those I chose will wish to stay.*

Affirm in your mind that you are sensual and attractive. Focus on the aspects of yourself that you like. Play music that makes you feel good according to your taste, mood, and desired results of the spell. Burn incense or use essential oils that correspond to love, sensuality, and friendship such as jasmine, rose, or lavender. Enter the bath or shower, relax, and continue to focus on your positive attributes. Make sure every part of your body is immersed in the water at least once. If you are in a shower, use the washcloth with the salt to wash your body. Close your eyes and listen to the music, confirm your worthiness, and say: *I have many gifts to share, I tend myself with love and care. Friends and loves will find their way, to come to me this very day!* Intuitively add whatever words of power you feel are appropriate. When you are finished visualizing and affirming your worth, continue to bathe or shower as you normally would. When you are finished, relax and repeat the words of power. If you make this a regular weekly ritual, consider using a favorite soap you've chosen for its magical attributes from the herbs or oils it contains. Enjoy a favorite beverage while you relax, or use a special towel you use only for this spell. This spell can also be cast with good friends, partners, and lovers to bond and build up each other's confidence.

Learn something new.
Color: Yellow-Green

Monday 12

☽→♉ 12:44 pm
International Day of Human Space Flight

Tuesday 13

Scrabble Day

Wednesday 14

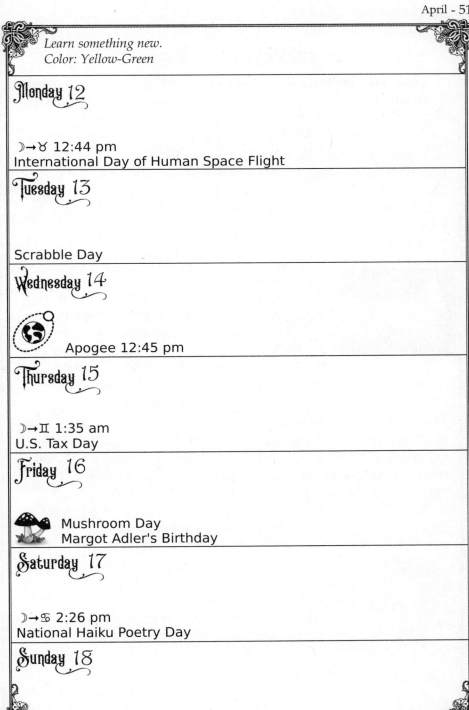

Apogee 12:45 pm

Thursday 15

☽→♊ 1:35 am
U.S. Tax Day

Friday 16

Mushroom Day
Margot Adler's Birthday

Saturday 17

☽→♋ 2:26 pm
National Haiku Poetry Day

Sunday 18

Exploring the Elements

Reading about the Classical Elements[3] is a great way to gather knowledge, but true wisdom and insight come from experience. Try doing things that will help you explore each element. Below are some suggestions to get you started on your adventures.

Air: Make friends with the wind by flying a kite, playing disc golf, blowing bubbles (see page 20), or casting a wish spell with a dandelion. To do a dandelion wish spell, simply visualize your goal, focus your intent, and then send the energy forth on the winds by blowing the fluffy seeds off a dandelion.

Fire: Try your skill at ceromancy (also called carromancy). This is a form of divination by which you pour melted wax into cold water and interpret the wax's movements and formations. You might also try lighting a campfire with the power of the Sun through a magnifying glass or clear crystal sphere and of course, candles will always help you connect with fire.

Water: Swimming, bobbing for apples, kayaking and canoeing, and other water-based sports are the obvious adventures here, but you might also try exploring natural formation created by water such as cave formations or canyons. Hag stones are also formed by water and you can carry one along with a shell to help you connect to this element. Of course, visiting natural springs, the ocean, or other body of water is a great place to start.

Earth: Gardening outdoors or tending to a windowsill herb garden is a great way to connect with the Earth. Ferns and ivy correspond to the Earth element and are great houseplants. Take a guided cave tour or bury yourself in the sand on a beach.

Life Hack: For a quick, low-calorie, thin-crust pizza, spread pizza sauce on a tortilla, add your favorite pizza toppings and shredded cheese. Bake at 375 for about 10 minutes or until browned and bubbly.

Shield yourself from the emotions of others.
Color: Yellow-Orange

Monday 19

☉→♉ 3:34 pm

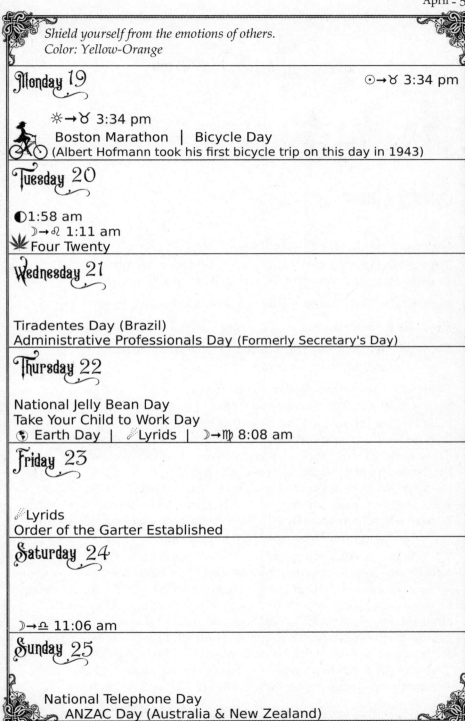

☿→♉ 3:34 pm
Boston Marathon | Bicycle Day
(Albert Hofmann took his first bicycle trip on this day in 1943)

Tuesday 20

◐1:58 am
☽→♌ 1:11 am
Four Twenty

Wednesday 21

Tiradentes Day (Brazil)
Administrative Professionals Day (Formerly Secretary's Day)

Thursday 22

National Jelly Bean Day
Take Your Child to Work Day
🜨 Earth Day | ⸭Lyrids | ☽→♍ 8:08 am

Friday 23

⸭Lyrids
Order of the Garter Established

Saturday 24

☽→♎ 11:06 am

Sunday 25

National Telephone Day
ANZAC Day (Australia & New Zealand)

May Overview

May is National Bike Month, Lupus Awareness Month, Foster Care Month, and National Barbecue Month.

Study Guide

Runes: ᚺ Hagalaz, ᚾ Naudhiz

Tarot: *Major Arcana:* Justice, Hermit *Minor Arcana:* Five of Wands, Five of Cups, Five of Pentacles, Five of Swords

Botanicals: Bay, Thyme, Rue, Lavender, Hyssop, Poppy

Crystals & Stones: Cat's Eye, Tiger's Eye, Hawk's Eye, Moonstone

Deities: Hel, Apollo, The Tuatha Dé Danann, Horus, Quetzalcoatl, Kannon

Exercise: Close your eyes and visualize a bubble surrounding you. This bubble extends through everything including the ground (A), and below your feet. You may draw a boundary (B) where your sphere intersects the ground to help you with visu-  alization, and this is often used even by experienced covens to assist with precise visualization. This is a basic skill used by magical practi- tioners when *casting a circle* to help *contain* energy you raise within the circle and *protect* you from outside energy.

As you become skilled at this visual exercise, or if you are already an experienced practitioner, flex your mental muscles by visu- alizing the sphere changing colors from swirling violet-colored energy to blue, then green, yellow, orange, and red. For a great protection circle, imagine that your sphere is made of a flexible membrane-like gelatin that you can see through but is metallic on the outside like reflective sunglasses. Take this exercise even further by shrinking your sphere down to a small ball that fits in your hand (C) and the expanding it back out to surround you.

More Information: PracticalWitch.com/May

May

1 ⊛ Sabbat

2

3 Last quarter

4

5 ⊕ Exact Cross-Quarter 1:36 am

6

7

8

9

10

11 New

12

13

14

15

16

17

18

19 First Quarter

20

21

22

23

24

25

26 Full

27

28

29

30

31

Beltane Sabbat

This Sabbat is a celebration of the uniting of Earth and Sun. The light of the Sun has grown stronger and its warmth has fully awakened the Earth. Fertility and abundance are primary themes for rituals, and spells for harmony and unification are often cast. The color green is used in candles, clothing, and body paint.

Altars are adorned with seasonal fruits and vegetables along with fresh flowers and herbs. We make flower chains and wreaths, wearing them like crowns. Many rituals include a Maypole Dance and decorating a besom with flowers. Some Witches leave offerings for the nature spirits or fae. May baskets[7] filled with flowers and sweet treats are sometimes left on the doorsteps of friends.

This is a time of magic and celebration of the lush fertility of the Earth. You can feel magical energy crackle in the air, especially in locations surrounded by nature such as woods, parks, and open spaces away from "civilization". If you are celebrating Samhain in the Southern Hemisphere right now, see page 118.

Maypole Dance[8]

Money isn't security.
Color: Purple

Monday 26

☽→♏ 11:19 am
Super[9] ○♏ 10:31 pm
National Pretzel Day
ANZAC Day observed (Australia & New Zealand)

Tuesday 27

Perigee 10:22 am
National Tell a Story Day

Wednesday 28

☽→♐ 10:43 am
National Superhero Day

Thursday 29

National Zipper Day
Shōwa Day (Japan)

Friday 30

☽→♑ 11:16 am
International Jazz Day
Beltane Eve (Walpurgisnacht)
Arbor Day / Tree Day *-plant a tree in honor of your favorite deity*

Saturday 1

Sabbat: Beltane/Samhain
WitchAcademy.org founded 1996
Loyalty Day | Kentucky Derby | Law Day | Lei Day
Herb Day | Labor Day/May Day (Brazil & Mexico) | EOD Day[10]

Sunday 2

☽→♒ 2:31 pm

Brood X

This year we will experience the return of Brood X (ten), a generation of 17-year cycle cicadas of the Magicicada genus. We were last visited by Brood X in 2004, and this is the same brood mentioned in Bob Dylan's 1970 song *Day of the Locusts*. They will begin to emerge in the eastern United States as soon as the soil about 8-inches down warms to 64°. This is when you'll see irises blooming and most deciduous trees have their leaves. Billions of these curious creatures will complete one of their life cycles by tunneling up from the soil in huge masses. Once emerged they will lay eggs on the branches of trees and die a few weeks later. This usually begins when deciduous trees have most of their new leaves and early iris flowers are blooming. We will hear their songs from late mornings to just after sunset until July.

The emergence of Brood X can be shocking for uninformed people, and they are often confused with swarming locusts. Watching social media around this event should be entertaining. For the record, locusts are green and are more like grasshoppers while cicadas are more like crickets. The confusion between the two began with early North American colonists. Periodical cicadas are only found in North America and colonists had only their religious education about locusts and plagues from the Bible so they assumed that these massive groups of cicadas were the same.

Magic: Cicadas have no pupal state like moths and butterflies which undergo complete metamorphosis. Instead, they transform from one fully-functional period of their life cycle (instar) to the next through molting. Witches will sometimes use the discarded shells (cast-off exoskeletons) in **spells of transformation, rebirth, renewal, and personal change**. These gnome-like creatures are symbols of the Earth.

Gardens & Pets: Cicadas will suck plant juices, however, they normally do not cause the devastation that a locust swarm will. If you are planting trees, consider fall planting to avoid Brood X while they are here. Never try to poison cicadas because it won't do any good and may harm pets that tend to eat them. If your pet isn't having difficulty swallowing them, they won't do any harm to your furry family. Lawns might take some damage from dogs who will hear them in the soil and will start digging up lawns to find them.

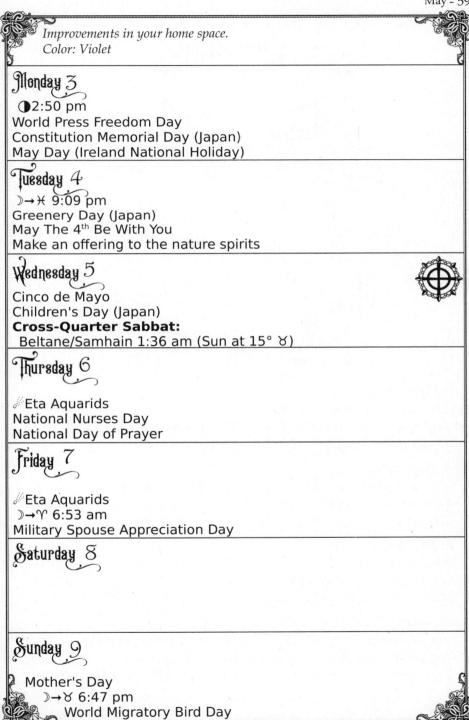

Improvements in your home space.
Color: Violet

Monday 3

☽2:50 pm
World Press Freedom Day
Constitution Memorial Day (Japan)
May Day (Ireland National Holiday)

Tuesday 4

☽→♓ 9:09 pm
Greenery Day (Japan)
May The 4th Be With You
Make an offering to the nature spirits

Wednesday 5

Cinco de Mayo
Children's Day (Japan)
Cross-Quarter Sabbat:
 Beltane/Samhain 1:36 am (Sun at 15° ♉)

Thursday 6

⋰Eta Aquarids
National Nurses Day
National Day of Prayer

Friday 7

⋰Eta Aquarids
☽→♈ 6:53 am
Military Spouse Appreciation Day

Saturday 8

Sunday 9

Mother's Day
 ☽→♉ 6:47 pm
  World Migratory Bird Day

Horoscopes

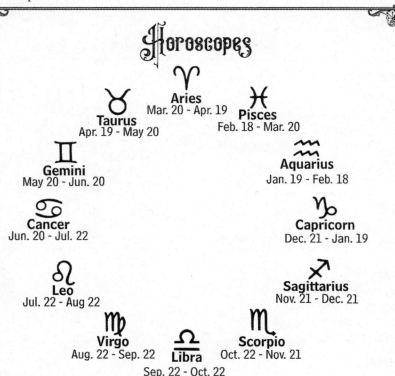

♈ **Aries**
Mar. 20 - Apr. 19

♓ **Pisces**
Feb. 18 - Mar. 20

♉ **Taurus**
Apr. 19 - May 20

♒ **Aquarius**
Jan. 19 - Feb. 18

♊ **Gemini**
May 20 - Jun. 20

♋ **Cancer**
Jun. 20 - Jul. 22

♑ **Capricorn**
Dec. 21 - Jan. 19

♌ **Leo**
Jul. 22 - Aug 22

♐ **Sagittarius**
Nov. 21 - Dec. 21

♍ **Virgo**
Aug. 22 - Sep. 22

♎ **Libra**
Sep. 22 - Oct. 22

♏ **Scorpio**
Oct. 22 - Nov. 21

♑ Capricorn

This year is all about finding your people and setting your pace to build a solid foundation. Your ambition and diplomacy both work in your favor socially and in career pursuits.

♒ Aquarius

Your humanitarian and altruistic skills become critical this year as many around you are in need. Remember to take time for yourself to avoid bottling up stress and ending up resentful.

♓ Pisces

This is a great year of psychic growth as you are learning to utilize your emphatic and sympathetic abilities to read people's true intentions. Try to stick to a regular schedule to stay on track.

♈ Aries

Your strong drive and initiative can pay off this year if you combine a casual interest into a charitable or entrepreneurial project. Temper your competitive nature by innovating.

Continued on page 62

You are not an emotional yo-yo.
Color: Deep Orange

Monday 10

Christopher Penezak's Birthday

Tuesday 11

● ♉ 1:59 pm
Apogee 4:53 pm
(Farthest for 2021)

Wednesday 12

☽→♊ 7:43 am
International Nurses' Day

Thursday 13

Ascension Day (National Holiday in Germany)

Friday 14

☽→♋ 8:31 pm
Gabriel D. Fahrenheit created Fahrenheit scale on this day in 1686.

Saturday 15

Armed Forces Day
National Bike to Work Day
Peace Officers Memorial Day

Sunday 16

Honor Our LGBT Elders Day

Continued from page 60

Horoscopes

♉ Taurus

Determination and thoroughness allow you to succeed at almost anything you put your mind to but beware of others mistaking your endurance for tolerance. Communicate with patience.

♊ Gemini

Your versatility helps you adapt to a quickly changing world this year as you learn to let go of indecision. Your quick-wit and abilities of persuasion can help expand your social network.

♋ Cancer

Understanding and nurturing by nature, you tend to be the protector of your people. Use your sympathetic and artistic skills to connect with others to avoid becoming clannish.

♌ Leo

Loyalty and a strong will make you the natural choice for leadership. Keep your ego and pride in check as you rise to positions of authority. People are looking to you this year to take the reins.

♍ Virgo

Use your natural analytical and studious abilities to apply yourself to the psychic and magical mysteries. You master skills quickly so don't get too critical of yourself in these intuitive pursuits.

♎ Libra

Balance and harmony are important for you to stay grounded. Keep the peace by learning to say *no* when you truly need to. Your natural charm will help you let them down easy.

♏ Scorpio

You are a conscientious individual with a strong sense of justice and fairness. Set aside specific times of the week to research the news and world events so the stress doesn't overwhelm you.

♐ Sagittarius

Let your good luck and honesty draw opportunities rather than playing the odds or taking risks this year. Travel may be limited and you may need to expand your horizons in creative ways.

Balance relationships.
Color: Pale Green

Monday 17

☽→♌ 7:44 am
View Mercury low on the western horizon just after sunset

Tuesday 18

Omar Khayyam's Birthday

Wednesday 19

●2:12 pm
Malcom X's Birthday
☽→♍ 4:00 pm
Emergency Medical Services for Children Day

Thursday 20

☉→♊ 2:38 pm

Friday 21

☽→♎ 8:36 pm
World Day of Cultural Diversity
National Defense Transportation Day
Gwyddion Pendderwen's Birthday

Saturday 22

National Maritime Day

Sunday 23

☽→♏ 10:01 pm
National Lucky Penny Day

Lunar Eclipse Magic

Check the maps on page 152 to see if this week's Total Lunar Eclipse is visible in your area. Don't worry if it isn't, an eclipse doesn't have to be visible for you to be able to work with its energy. This week there is a Total Lunar Eclipse on the 26th, and this is a great opportunity to experiment with Lunar Eclipse energy in magic.

There is a moment of apparent hesitation when a pendulum reaches the farthest arc in its swing just before it reverses back. The energy of an eclipse is similar to this and sensitive Witches may feel this as a time of stillness or hesitation Eclipses provide us with a time "between the worlds," or a window through which we can work interesting varieties of magic.

Throughout the Moon's cycle around the Earth[11], the Moon's light waxes and wanes. During a lunar eclipse, we experience the energy of multiple Moon phases. The Moon is always in its Full phase when a Lunar Eclipse occurs, then partially or completely hidden, and then visible again. Within a few minutes, the energy similar to a complete lunar cycle is present.

In addition to this cyclical energy, we are acutely aware of the Earth's presence. Her shadow falls across the Moon as she comes into position between the Moon and the Sun. This adds the unification of Earth and Moon energy, reinforcing the sense of wholeness, completion, and cycles of a lunar eclipse. You might find this an excellent time to focus on the Goddess, psychic skills, or work magic in harmony with this cyclic lunar energy.

When planning your magic to be harmonious with a lunar eclipse, consider the primary Full Moon energy first. As the eclipse begins, work on banishing and decrease, at the peak of the eclipse you can shift your focus to goals you would normally consider on the New or Dark Moon, and as the eclipse ends you are working with waxing moon energy again. Once the eclipse is over, you are back to the Full Moon. A good example of magic to perform during a lunar eclipse would be to work on your psychic skills. As the moon wanes during the eclipse, you could focus on ridding yourself of blocks. As it waxes back to full, you might focus on increasing your psychic skills.

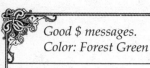

Good $ messages.
Color: Forest Green

Monday 24

Victoria Day
National Scavenger Hunt Day
Whit Monday (National Holiday in Germany)

Tuesday 25

 Perigee 8:50 pm
☽→♐ 9:40 pm
National Missing Children's Day

Wednesday 26

Super ○♐ 6:13 am
Total Lunar Eclipse

Thursday 27

☽→♑ 9:24 pm
Morning Glory Zell-Ravenheart's Birthday

Friday 28

Saturday 29

☿ ℞ 5.27 pm
☽→♒ 11:05 pm

Sunday 30

Joan of Arc Day

June Overview

June is LGBTQIA+ Pride Month, National Oceans Month, National Adopt a Cat Month, and Candy Month.

Study Guide

Runes: | Isa, ᛃ Jera

Tarot: *Major Arcana:* Wheel of Fortune, Strength *Minor Arcana:* Six of Wands, Six of Cups, Six of Pentacles, Six of Swords

Botanicals: Basil, Yarrow, Mint, Mugwort, Violet, Narcissus

Crystals & Stones: Amethyst, Zebra Stone, Aquamarine, Fluorite

Deities: Ceridwen, Magni, Set, Nuada, Áed, Clota

Exercise: Visualize a sphere as you did in May. Try to "feel" the sphere in the palm of your hand. Visualize the sphere growing larger, pushing through you as it grows. See it extend out around you until you are inside it. It extends down past the ground just like the circle casting in May's Study Guide. Next change the color of your sphere from red to orange, yellow, green, blue, indigo, and violet.

Once you've visualized all the colors, see the sphere shrink back down. See and feel it grown smaller until it fits into your hand again. When this is easy for you to visualize, go a step further during the large sphere phase. Open your eyes and "see" the circle around you. Using your finger, wand, or athame, pull the sphere back in. Drawn the energy of the sphere into yourself or your ritual tool as if you were vacuuming it up.

More Information: PracticalWitch.com/June

June

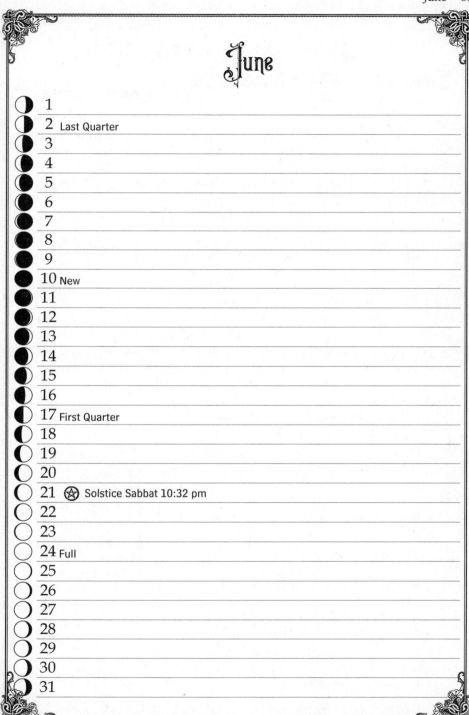

1

2 Last Quarter

3

4

5

6

7

8

9

10 New

11

12

13

14

15

16

17 First Quarter

18

19

20

21 Solstice Sabbat 10:32 pm

22

23

24 Full

25

26

27

28

29

30

31

Crafting a Witch's Ladder

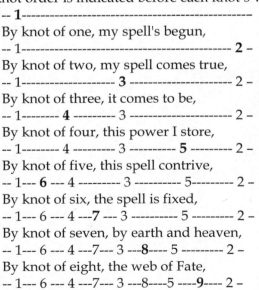

1   6   4   7   3   8   5   9   2

A Witch's Ladder[12] is a classic spell of the knot and cord classification. A string, cord, or rope is knotted while speaking a charm. Sometimes a feather or bead is tied into each knot. The ladder is then used as a type of fetish or talisman and can be worn around the neck or waist, hung in the home, buried, or stored in a spell box. A Witch's Ladder can be used to focus any magical intent from protection and love to prosperity and binding.

The picture on this page shows the order in which nine knots are tied. As each knot is tied the corresponding line of the spell is chanted. You can repeat each knot's charm three times while making the knot to assist your focus. Summon your will and intent as you tie each knot, and remember to use your visualization skills. Use your creativity to alter the original charm's wording to fit your needs, and feel free to tie charms into your cord. Remember to incorporate both contagion and similarity into your spell design. A helpful guide to the knot order is indicated before each knot's Words of Power.

-- **1**---
By knot of one, my spell's begun,
-- **1**--- **2** –
By knot of two, my spell comes true,
-- **1**-------------------- **3** ---------------------- **2** –
By knot of three, it comes to be,
-- **1**-------- **4** --------- 3 ---------------------- **2** –
By knot of four, this power I store,
-- **1**-------- 4 --------- 3 ---------- **5** --------- **2** –
By knot of five, this spell contrive,
-- **1**--- **6** --- 4 --------- 3 ---------- 5--------- **2** –
By knot of six, the spell is fixed,
-- **1**--- 6 --- 4 ---**7** --- 3 ---------- 5 --------- **2** –
By knot of seven, by earth and heaven,
-- **1**--- 6 --- 4 ---7--- 3 ---**8**--- 5 --------- **2** –
By knot of eight, the web of Fate,
-- **1**--- 6 --- 4 ---7--- 3 ---8---5 ----**9**---- **2** –
By knot of nine, the thing is mine!

Get creative! Tie feathers or charms into your knots.

An advanced variation of this spell using a Cairn is on page 78.

Realizations & Gratitude
  Color: White

Monday 31

Memorial Day (U.S. Federal)
Spring Bank Holiday in the United Kingdom

Tuesday 1

☽→♓ 4:08 am
National Go Barefoot Day

Wednesday 2

◑2:24 am

Thursday 3

☽→♈ 12:59 pm
Marion Zimmer Bradley's Birthday
National Repeat Day National Repeat Day

Friday 4

Saturday 5

World Environment Day

Sunday 6

D Day
☽→♉ 12:47 am

Solar Eclipse Magic

Check the maps on page 153 to see if this week's Annular Solar Eclipse on the 10th is visible in your area. Just like the Lunar Eclipse magic covered on page 64, an eclipse doesn't have to be visible for you to be able to work with its energy. This week's eclipse is a great time to experiment with Solar Eclipse energy in your magic.

Daylight hours increase and decrease throughout the year. The shortest day of the year is the Winter Solstice Sabbat. Hours of daylight increase as the months pass and near the Vernal Equinox Sabbat, day and night hours are equal[13]. The Summer Solstice Sabbat is the longest day of the year and from there the daylight wanes to be equal with the night again at the Autumnal Equinox Sabbat and back again to the Winter Solstice Sabbat.

During a solar eclipse, we experience what might be called a micro year. The Sun is whole, then partially or completely hidden, and then visible again. Within just a few minutes, an energy similar to a complete cycle of Solstices and Equinoxes can be felt while at the same time we become highly aware of the Moon's presence. Her shadow falls across the Earth as she comes into position between the Earth and the Sun. Solar and Lunar energy is united, reinforcing the sense of wholeness, completion, and cycles to a solar eclipse.

When planning your magic to be harmonious with a solar eclipse, consider that a solar eclipse can only occur during the day on a New Moon. This means that you are working with New Moon energy. An eclipse does not have to be visible for you to work magic with the eclipse energies. You won't be able to see every eclipse unless you can travel all over the world easily! Simply look up the data in your Almanac to find the exact time and date to work your magic.

Solar eclipses are perfect for some specific types of magic. At the beginning of a solar eclipse, you could focus on ridding yourself of unwanted energies, bad habits, unhealthy patterns of thinking and acting, negativity, and other baneful things in your life. As the eclipse passes you could bring into your focus the things you wish to grow in your life such as prosperity, positive thoughts and actions, and good health.

Make new victories.
Color: Purple

Monday 7

Vestalia Begins
Apogee 9:27 pm
British Museum Founded 1753

Tuesday 8

☽→♊ 1:48 pm
World Oceans Day
National Best Friend Day

Wednesday 9

National Strawberry Rhubarb Pie Day

Thursday 10

●♊ 5:52 am
National Iced Tea Day
Annular Solar Eclipse 5:42 am

Friday 11

☽→♋ 2:23 am

Saturday 12

Anne Frank's Birthday

Sunday 13

☽→♌ 1:23 pm
Gerald Gardner's Birthday

Midsummer Sabbat

Midsummer or Litha is the Summer Solstice. It is the time of the year when the Sun is at the peak of its power and marks the longest day of the year. Although this is officially the first day of summer, the days will grow shorter from now until Yule. Potions, ale, mead, and other delights are brewed at this time of year, and spells of protection and revitalization are cast. We also keep in mind that with lush fertility comes death as the Sun begins to wane. If you are celebrating Yule in the Southern Hemisphere right now, see page 138.

Illustration adapted from *The Lancashire Witches* by William Harrison Ainsworth, 1849.

Easy Fudge Recipe

Mix one can sweetened condensed milk (14 ounces) and 3 cups chocolate chips (about 18 ounces) in a large bowl and heat in the microwave for 3 minutes. Stir and return to microwave, this time stirring every 60 seconds. When all the chocolate has melted, add 1 teaspoon vanilla extract, mix well and pour into a 9-inch pan lined with parchment or wax paper. Chill for 3 hours in the refrigerator, cut, and serve.

Variations of this recipe are very easy and you can have a lot of fun using your creativity! Add 3-6 drops peppermint oil or 3-9 drops of orange oil for interesting flavors. You can use butterscotch, cherry, mint, or peanut butter chips instead of chocolate chips, and for Sabbats, I often make one batch of chocolate and one batch of peanut butter and then swirl them together as pictured. If you prefer your fudge to be firm and remain stable outside of the refrigerator, you can add more chocolate to the recipe. In the U.S. most chips come in 12-ounce bags so I just use two and make it with 24 ounces. This extra chocolate technique is especially helpful when sending your fudge in gift packages. You can make a very creamy version by using milk chocolate chips, or try stirring in nuts, chopped up cookies, marshmallows, or dried fruits like cherries or blueberries just before spreading it into the pan to firm up.

Take a little risk.
Color: Turquoise

Monday 14

Flag Day
World Blood Donor Day

Tuesday 15

☽→♍ 11:02 pm
National Fudge Day
Nature Photography Day | Vestalia Ends

Wednesday 16

Thursday 17

☾10:54 pm
Starhawk's Birthday

Friday 18

☽→♎ 3:54 am
National Go Fishing Day

Saturday 19

Juneteenth

Sunday 20

☽→♏ 6:58 am
Solstice Sabbat: Litha/Yule (☉→♋ 10:32 pm)
Father's Day | World Refugee Day | American Eagle Day

Crafting a Magical Cairn

Stacked stones called "cairn" (pronounced kârn - sounding like the name Karen) are traditional formations created to mark paths. You can use a cairn in your yard, next to your door, or on your altar. They make wonderful protection wards, and you can imbue them with any energy as you focus and balance the stones.

By combining the stacking of stones to make a cairn with the classic Witch's Ladder spell, you can make a cairn for any purpose. This is a great activity for equinox Sabbats like Ostara and Mabon when day and night hang in the balance. The same techniques used to create a Witch's Ladder (see page 68) can be applied to creating a magical cairn. Simply replace the word *knot* from the Witches Ladder spell with the word *stone*.

Tumbled, semi-precious stones such as rose quartz or amethyst can be used for their magical correspondence. You might prefer to use the more traditional flat river rocks or black "hot rocks" used for massage therapy. Try changing the other words in the Witch's Ladder spell to suit your specific intent. Here is an example of a cairn spell created to keep one sure-footed on their own spiritual path.

Do not create cairns in public spaces or near waterways as they can cause hikers to get lost or disrupt the ecosystem.

By stone of one, my path's begun,
By stone of two, I'll make it through,
By stone of three, allow me to see,
By stone of four, past every door,
By stone of five, I'll always thrive,
By stone of six, my footing fixèd,
By stone of seven, I'll use what's given,
By stone of eight, I make my fate,
By stone of nine, my path I'll find.

FYI: To undo a Witch's Ladder, untie the knots
in reverse order in which they were tied.

Rest & Recover
Color: Gray

Monday 21

International Day of Yoga

Tuesday 22

☽→♐ 7:56 am
☿ Direct 3:56 pm

Wednesday 23

Perigee 4:54 am
Public Service Day

Thursday 24

☽→♑ 8:05 am
○♑ 1:39 pm
Janet Farrar's Birthday

Friday 25

Day of the Seafarer
Take Your Dog to Work Day

Saturday 26

☽→♒ 9:09 am
National Canoe Day

Sunday 27

Helen Keller's Birthday

July Overview

July is National Ice Cream Month and National Cell Phone Courtesy Month.

Study Guide

Runes: ᛇ Eihwaz, ᛈ Pertho

Tarot: *Major Arcana:* The Hanged Man, Death
Minor Arcana: Seven of Wands, Seven of Cups, Seven of Pentacles, Seven of Swords

Botanicals: Elder, Nettle, Hibiscus, Pepper, Yew, Feverfew

Crystals & Stones: Sapphire, Emerald, Diamond, Wavellite

Deities: Balder, Atlas, Angau, Osiris, Chernobog, Altjira

Exercise: Try designing a spell using similarity (page 36) and contagion (page 40) creatively. Instead of crafting a spell with elemental correspondences (as on page 32), try designing your spell around the five senses. An example can be made with the scenario of you finding a house for sale that fits you perfectly. You submit your bid and want to help manifest your dream with a little magic[14]. While touring the house you collected some spell ingredients: a pinch of soil that smells like "home" (smell), a recording of the sound of the doorbell on your phone (hearing), a picture of the house or satellite map view that you've printed out (sight), a cookie served at the open house (taste), and a small piece of loose carpet fiber (touch).

Note that each of these items corresponds to your target. The soil, cookie, doorbell, and carpet are obvious contagion aspects, and the picture is a great example of similarity. To perform this spell, relax, and practice your box breathing (page 16) and cast your circle (page 58). Design words of power as you prefer and put each item into a jar or spell bag to carry as a charm. Play the sound of the doorbell into the jar or bag just before you close close the lid or tie the bag shut.

More Information: PracticalWitch.com/July

July

1 Last Quarter
2
3
4
5
6
7
8
9 New
10
11
12
13
14
15
16
17 First Quarter
18
19
20
21
22
23 Full
24
25
26
27
28
29
30
31 Last Quarter

The Witch's Alphabet

The Witch's Alphabet is also known at the Witches Runes or Theban Script. It is an alphabet used by Witches as a substitution cipher. This is a simple encryption method that replaces one character with another in a pattern. It is intended to prevent prying eyes from reading private entries in Books of Shadows (BoS) or spell book and lends an air of mystery to writing.

Theban Script

A	B	C	D	E	F	G
H	I	J	K	L	M	N
O	P	Q	R	S	T	U
V	W	X	Y	Z		

The Theban alphabet does not exactly translate to the English alphabet because the letters W, J, and U were not used in Middle Latin. You can create characters to replace these letters, or you may substitute the character for I in place of J, and the character for V in place of W and U. These substitutions are widely accepted and practiced by many Witches.

The Theban Alphabet first appeared in the book entitled, *The Magus*. The English occult and Kabbalah scholar, Francis Barrett, published The Magus in 1801. In the book, the alphabet is attributed to Honorius II (Pope from 1216 to 1227). Many medieval grimoires were said to have been written by Honorius II. The legend quoted from The Magus states:

"The Mysterious Characters of Letters deliver'd by Honorius call'd the Theban Alphabet." Honorius II had the reputation of being a magician and was said to have sponsored a crusade to Egypt."

Punctuation is not normally used with Theban Script, however, a tilda (~) can be attractive at the end of sentences when using the script.

Talk to a friend.
Color: Bright Royal Blue

Monday 28

☽→♓ 12:51 pm
Scott Cunningham's Birthday
Stewart Farrar's Birthday

Tuesday 29

National Camera Day

Wednesday 30

☽→♈ 8:22 pm
International Asteroid Day

Thursday 1

●4:10 pm
International Joke Day
Canada Day (Canadian National Holiday)

Friday 2

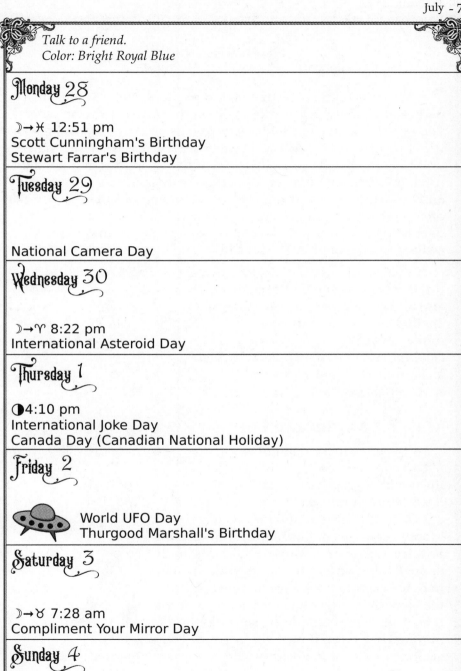

World UFO Day
Thurgood Marshall's Birthday

Saturday 3

☽→♉ 7:28 am
Compliment Your Mirror Day

Sunday 4

Independence Day (U.S. Federal)

Mandrake Magic

Mandrake is a powerful magical plant, like many others in the nightshade family (*Solanaceae*). Although it doesn't scream when you pull it from the ground as legend tells us, it can be a very tricky plant to grow. Although there are five species in the Mandrake genus (*Mandragora*), there are only two species traditionally used in Witchcraft. European Mandrake (*Mandragora officinarum*) and Womandrake or Autumn Drake (*Mandragora autumnalis*). Like other nightshades, it contains toxic tropane alkaloids along with over 80 other chemicals. Among the most toxic chemicals are atropine, belladonnine, hyoscyamine, and scopolamine (hyoscine).

You should never consume any part of the plant, but **the dried roots make incredibly powerful charms and add extra power to any magical spell.** Don't confuse true mandrake (*Mandragora*) with American Mandrake or Mayapple, which is an entirely different genus and species (*Podophyllum peltatum*).

Making Mandrake Oil

If you are lucky enough to obtain a piece of root, put it into a jar filled with a good base or carrier oil. After letting it infuse into the oil for at least one cycle of the Moon (Full Moon to Full Moon) use drops of the oil to **anoint candles, jewelry, talismans, amulet, altar tools, mojo or spell bags, or use a drop on your third eye to help open up your psychic powers**. Store the oil in the refrigerator so it doesn't become rancid, and consider adding some liquid Vitamin E to help keep it fresh for years. Substitute alcohol for the oil to preserve it for even longer periods.

Depiction of Mandrake adapted from a 1583 botanical illustration[15].

Be Practical.
Color: Deep Navy Blue

Monday 5

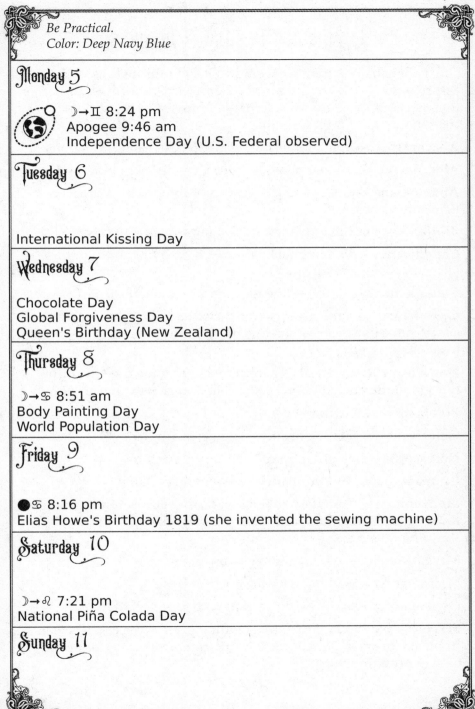

☽→♊ 8:24 pm
Apogee 9:46 am
Independence Day (U.S. Federal observed)

Tuesday 6

International Kissing Day

Wednesday 7

Chocolate Day
Global Forgiveness Day
Queen's Birthday (New Zealand)

Thursday 8

☽→♋ 8:51 am
Body Painting Day
World Population Day

Friday 9

●♋ 8:16 pm
Elias Howe's Birthday 1819 (she invented the sewing machine)

Saturday 10

☽→♌ 7:21 pm
National Piña Colada Day

Sunday 11

Divination & The Omancies

People have sought answers and insight through wildly assorted means. We've all heard of tarot cards, a form of cartomancy, but there are some rather obscure forms of the "omancies" you might find interesting.

Abacomancy – divination using dust, ashes, or sand formations

Aleuromancy – divination with flour, a very ancient practiced

Apantomancy – interpreting chance encounters with animals or items found nearby.

Bibliomancy or Stichomancy – random passages in books

Capnomancy – divination using smoke, commonly from incense (also known as knissomancy).

Cledonomancy – Interpreting random words overheard in passing

Cleromancy – a large group of omancies including the casting of *lots* or items like dice (astragalomancy), beans (favomancy), bones (osteomancy), etc.

Dowsing or Radiesthesia – a group including the use of pendulums (pallomancy), divining rods (rhabdomancy/water witching)

Entomancy – divination by insects

Geloscopy – divination from the sounds of laughter

Horoscopy – divination from Zodiac natal positions

Lampadomancy or Pyromancy – divination of flames

Mediaomancy[16] – modern divination forms such as tuning into the radio or watching random videos (see cledonomancy) or through shuffling music on a device (shufflemancy)

Margaritomancy – divination by bouncing pearls

Necromancy – speaking with the dead

Ovomancy or Ooscopy – divination with eggs

Scrying – another large group including gazing into crystals (gastromancy or crystallomancy), mirrors (catoptromancy), or pools of water (hydromancy)

Juggling material things.
Color: Light Violet

Monday 12

Henry David Thoreau Born 1817

Tuesday 13

☽→♍ 3:31 am
Margaret Murray's Birthday

Wednesday 14

Bastille Day

Thursday 15

☽→♎ 9:32 am
National Give Something Away Day

Friday 16

Saturday 17

●5:10 am
☽→♏ 1:39 pm
World Emoji Day
Paul Stamets Birthday (mycologist)

Sunday 18

Nelson Mandela Day

Understanding the Zodiac

Below is a diagram to help you understand what it really means when we refer to the Sun entering a Zodiac sign. From our position on Earth at the June Solstice, the Sun appears to be entering the Zodiac constellation of Cancer ♋. In late May it was in Gemini ♊. As the month progresses we move widdershins around the Zodiac entering Leo ♌ on July 22nd.

Your Zodiac Sign is also known as your Sun Sign. When you were born, the Sun appeared in the corresponding Zodiac's constellation. Your rising sign is the constellation that was on the horizon at sunrise at the location of your birth. Rising signs are also known as ascendants.

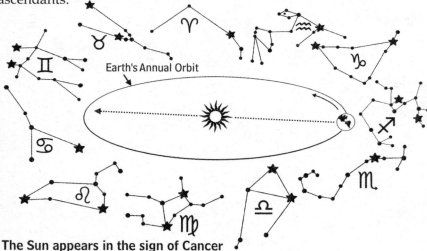

Earth's Annual Orbit

The Sun appears in the sign of Cancer on the June Solstice Sabbat

Symbols Used for Protection

Witch's Knot   Pentacle   Triquetra

Third-party interference.
Color: Light Blue

Monday 19

☽→♐ 4:08 pm
Sea Day (Japan)
San Francisco Public Library Begins Lending Books 1880

Tuesday 20

Moon Day[17]

Wednesday 21

 ☽→♑ 5:37 pm
Perigee 5:23 am

Thursday 22

☉→♌ 9:27 am

Friday 23

☽→♒ 7:13 pm
○♒ 9:36 pm
Eileen M. Collins becomes the 1st ♀ to command a space shuttle

Saturday 24

National Drive-Thru Day

Sunday 25

☽→♓ 10:30 pm
Parents' Day

August Overview

August is National Picnic Month and Water Quality Month.

Study Guide

Runes: ᛉ Elhaz, ᛋ Sowilo

Tarot: *Major Arcana:* Temperance, The Devil *Minor Arcana:* Eight of Wands, Eight of Cups, Eight of Pentacles, Eight of Swords

Botanicals: Star Anise, Pennyroyal, Patchouli, Garlic, Goldenseal

Crystals & Stones: Ruby, Pyrite, Lodestone (magnetite), Apatite

Deities: Lugh, Heimdall, Zeus, Áine, Thoth, Shango

Exercise: By now you've learned enough about crafting your magic to design a glamoury perfume. A glamour is usually classified as a beauty spell, but it doesn't change your physical appearance. They do help to influence how others perceive you and how you see yourself.

Do a little research on the magical correspondences of plants and aromatherapy uses of oils to find three essential oils that correspond to confidence and attraction such as the example below. Compose your words of power and do some box breathing to help you enter a relaxed magical state. Cast your circle and combine the three oils and use it as a perfume when you need a boost of confidence, wish to make new friends, or want to attract a partner.

Confidence & Attraction Oil

2 parts Ylang Ylang essential oil or absolutely
1 part Patchouli essential oil
10 parts Bergamot essential oil
20 parts Avocado, Apricot, Jojoba, or Olive carrier oil

Use as a glamoury perfume or to anoint spell candles.

More Information & Plant Correspondences at:
PracticalWitch.com/August

August

1 ⊕ Sabbat
2
3
4
5
6
7 ⊕ Exact Cross-Quarter 1:53 am
8 New
9
10
11
12
13
14
15 First Quarter
16
17
18
19
20
21
22 Full (Blue)
23
24
25
26
27
28
29
30 Last Quarter
31

Lughnasadh or Lammas Sabbat

August 1st is the traditional beginning of Lughnasadh in the Northern Hemisphere. In the Southern Hemisphere, many Witches celebrate Imbolc at this time (see page 26). The two Sabbats are on opposite sides of the Wheel of the Year and this reflects the seasonal celebrations on opposite sides of the world.

This is the first of three harvest Sabbats and although some Witches celebrate the god Lugh, even more Witches celebrate this Sabbat by baking bread and showing gratitude for the grain harvest. When Lughnasadh was later adopted by the Christian church, it became Lammas and was associated with bread (Lammas meaning loaf-mass). However, a more harmonious celebration in tune with the natural cycles in most areas is to celebrate the first harvest of herbs, fruits, and vegetables.

No matter what you call this Sabbat, it is an excellent time to harvest magical or medicinal herbs and to figure out what you want to learn through the rest of the year (it is back-to-school time in many areas). Baking is always popular, and using a solar oven can become a great tradition to establish in your practice while harnessing the power of the Sun.

Lughnasadh is a traditional time to practice all types of crafts. Flip through your almanac to find recipes and projects to inspire you. You might enjoy making corn dollies to adorn your altar or use it as a poppet. Use fresh, green corn husks or buy tamale corn husks and soak them in warm water for a few minutes.

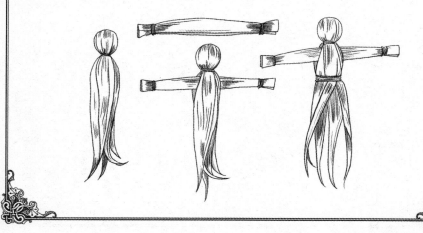

Delays
Color: Light Green

Monday 26

National Bagelfest Day

Tuesday 27

Wednesday 28

)→♈ 4:58 am
Delta Aquarids

Thursday 29

Delta Aquarids

Friday 30

)→♉ 3:08 pm
National Cheesecake Day
World (International) Friendship Day

Saturday 31

◑8:15 am

Sunday 1

Sabbat: Lughnasadh/Imbolc
Jerry Garcia's Birthday

American Harvests

The primary crops of indigenous groups in North America are squash, beans, and corn (maize). Together these are known as **The Three Sisters**. As foraging gave way to agriculture thousands of years ago, this trinity of plants emerged and spread from Mesoamerica.

Chili peppers came from the Americas, and Spanish conquerors brought the tomato plant from Central America back to Europe. This means that our beloved Italian marinara didn't even exist before the 16th century! Even that might pale in comparison to the American contributions of chocolate, vanilla, and blueberries to the culinary world.

A long list of herbs and spices come from the Americas. How could gumbo exist without Filè (Sassafras albidum)? Cheddar cheese wouldn't be very golden without Annatto seeds (Bixa orellana), and both Lemon Verbena (Lippia citriodora) and Allspice (*Pimenta dioica*) are used extensively in food and magic.

Sumac Lemonade

Sumac makes a wonderful lemonade-like tea that is high if Vitamin C. Purchase dried sumac berries or collect your own. Be absolutely certain you collect the red berries from *Rhus glabra* and not berries from poison sumac (*Toxicodendron vernix*) which contains urushiol – the same oily toxin in poison ivy. Soak berries in water overnight at a ratio of about 1 cup fresh berries (1/3 cup dried) to 1 quart of water. **Optional**: You can add 2 Tablespoons dried Lemon Verbena before steeping if you have some on hand or the juice of half a lemon. Strain the next day through a coffee filter or cheesecloth and sweeten the tea to taste. If it is too tangy for you, add a bit more water.

New projects may bring $
Color: Chartreuse

Monday 2

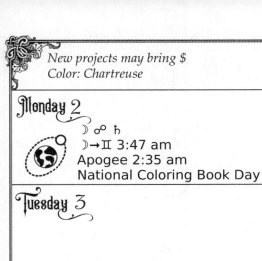

☽ ☌ ♄
☽→♊ 3:47 am
Apogee 2:35 am
National Coloring Book Day

Tuesday 3

Grab Some Nuts Day

Wednesday 4

☽→♋ 4:17 pm

Thursday 5

Mars Curiosity Rover sings happy birthday to itself[18]

Friday 6

Saturday 7

☽→♌ 2:32 am
Purple Heart Day
Campfire Day (and Night)
Sabbat: Cross Quarter 1:53 am (Sun at 15° ♌)

Sunday 8

● ♌ 8:49 am

Incense Recipes

Purification Incense

This recipe is perfect for cleansing and clearing an area, crystals or magical tools.

2 part Copal resin, broken into rice size bits.
4 parts dried Rosemary leaves
1 part ground Sage leaves

Dragon's Blood Incense

Use this for purification, protection, and to add power to spells. Use a mortar and pestle to break up resins into even pieces about the size of a lentil.

16 parts white Sandalwood chips
2 parts Dragon's Blood resin
2 parts Copal resin
1 part ground Cloves
1 part ground Cinnamon

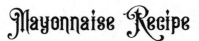

Mayonnaise Recipe

Making mayonnaise is a great way to learn about emulsions, and if you can make it, you can make a lotion. When choosing an acid to use, try regular vinegar, lemon juice, or any combination thereof. If you use mirin (sweetened rice vinegar), omit the sugar. Use any oil such as sunflower, olive, canola, corn, or any combination of these.

1 Egg Yolk*
½ tsp. Sea Salt   3 tbl. Acid (see instructions)
1 tsp. Sugar   1 cup Vegetable Oil
½ tsp. Powdered Mustard Seeds

Whisk together everything in the left column along with 1 tbl. of the acid. While continuing to whisk, add the oil a few drops at a time until the mixture begins to lighten from emulsification. Now you can *drizzle a fine stream of the rest of the oil* while continuing to whisk. When you've drizzled about half of the oil, add the remaining acid and return to oil drizzling and whisking.

* The FDA requires this consumer advisory: Consuming raw or undercooked eggs may increase your risk of foodborne illness.

Embrace change.
Color: Pale Indigo (faded denim)

Monday 9

☽→♍ 9:56 am
National Book Lovers Day

Tuesday 10

Lazy Day

Wednesday 11

☽→♎ 3:08 pm
Presidential Joke Day
Mountain Day (Japan)

Thursday 12

Perseids

Friday 13

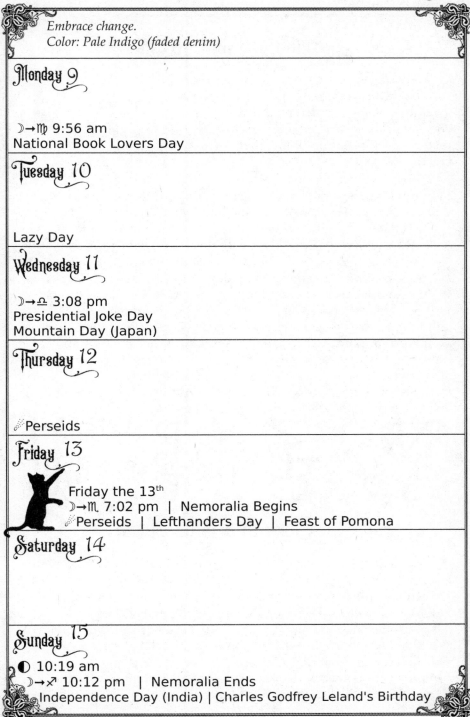

Friday the 13th
☽→♏ 7:02 pm | Nemoralia Begins
Perseids | Lefthanders Day | Feast of Pomona

Saturday 14

Sunday 15

☽ 10:19 am
☽→♐ 10:12 pm | Nemoralia Ends
Independence Day (India) | Charles Godfrey Leland's Birthday

Sigils & Bind Runes

A bindrune is a ligature of two or more runes joined together to form a single glyph. You can create your own bind rune by choosing runes based on your spiritual or magical needs and combining them in creative ways.

ᛒ + ᚺ = **ᛒ**

The Bluetooth logo is a bindrune created from Berkano and Hagalaz

A sigil is a similar ligature style created by combining the letters in phrases or keywords that express your will and intent. There are many methods used to create sigils and some of them are quite complex. A practical approach works just as well and it is easy to experiment with this intuitive magical technique.

State your goal with the fewest, most direct words possible. You can use the phrase *I am protected* or simply the word *protection* as use in this example to create a sigil for a protection spell. Sigils can be written on paper, inscribed into the wax of spell-candles, or painted on to stones that correspond to your goal. Eliminate all the vowels in your word or phrase. This results in prtctn. Now eliminate any repeating letters resulting in prtcn. Use these letters to make a creative glyph. Below are some examples of using these five letters. Feel free to rotate letters as desired to suit the vibe of your sigil design. The last sigil on the right was created using Theban Script (page 78).

Once in a Blue Moon

"Once in a Blue Moon" is a phrase that generally refers to a rare event. However, there are two types of actual Blue Moons.

* Seasonal Blue Moons occur every few years when there are four Full Moons within an astrological season (defined as the period between a Solstice and an Equinox). The third of these four is known as a Blue Moon such as the one on August 22, 2021. The next *seasonal* Blue Moon is August 19, 2024.

* Monthly Blue Moons refer to a second Full Moon in a calendar month. The next *monthly* Blue Moon will be on August 30, 2023.

Some compromise keeps the flow.
Color: Burgundy

Monday 16

Tuesday 17

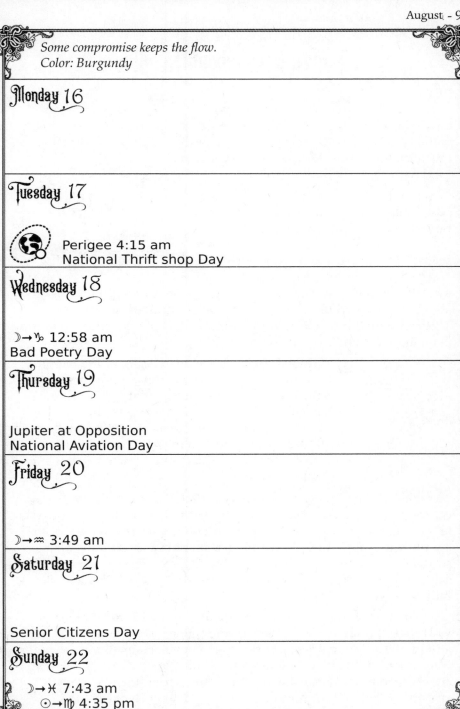

Perigee 4:15 am
National Thrift shop Day

Wednesday 18

☽→♑ 12:58 am
Bad Poetry Day

Thursday 19

Jupiter at Opposition
National Aviation Day

Friday 20

☽→♒ 3:49 am

Saturday 21

Senior Citizens Day

Sunday 22

☽→♓ 7:43 am
☉→♍ 4:35 pm
Seasonal Blue ○♒ 7:01 am (page 94)

Harvest Celebration Meal

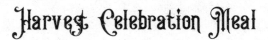

The *American Harvests* article (page 90) covers many extraordinary contributions of the North and South American continents to the culinary world. You can explore some of these plants by preparing this meal for any of the three harvest Sabbats: Lughnasadh, Mabon, and Samhain.

For this meal, you will need a winter-type squash. This can be acorn, butternut, pumpkin, hubbard, kabocha, or similar varieties. Peel the squash and remove the seeds[19]. Cut the squash into 1-2 inch cubes and toss in 2 tablespoons oil and 1 teaspoon sea salt. Skewer onto kebab sticks or place into mesh grilling basket and grill over medium heat until cooked to your desired softness. This can sometimes take about 45 minutes, so I often start them in the oven indoors and finish them on the grill.

When the squash seems to be about fifteen minutes away from being done, put 4-6 full ears of corn on the grill. Heat them fully for about 10 minutes. Grasp half of the leaves and corn silk and peel back to expose the kernels as pictured. Return to the grill with the squash and add mesquite wood to the charcoals to smoke everything for a few more minutes if desired.

Remove the squash and corn from the grill. Husk the corn and cut the kernels off the cob. To the corn kernels, add a large jar of your favorite tomato salsa and a can of your favorite beans. Tepary beans are the most traditional, but I often use black beans or pintos. The squash is ready to serve after you salt it to taste. Serve it with the salsa and corn chips. You can also puree the squash with coconut milk to serve as a hot or cold soup.

The squash itself is a main dish, but if you wish to add meat to your meal, turkey is also an American original, as are potatoes if you would like additional sides. For dessert, consider something on the true American theme with chocolate, vanilla, or blueberry (a North American native). To stick with the theme, serve sumac lemonade (recipe on page 94) or hot cocoa with a small pinch of cayenne.

Rebuild
Color: Green

Monday 23

Vulcanalia
Ride the Wind Day

Tuesday 24

☽→♈ 1:57 pm
Vesuvius Day

Wednesday 25

Thursday 26

☽→♉ 11:27 pm
Women's Equality Day

Friday 27

Just Because Day

Saturday 28

Sunday 29

☽→♊ 11:42 am
Apogee 9:22 pm

September Overview

September is Civic Awareness Month, National Wilderness Month, National Courtesy Month, Chicken Month, Self Improvement Month, Honey Month. National Hispanic Heritage Month begins on September 15th and ends next month on October 15th.

Study Guide

Runes: ↑ Tiwaz, ᛒ Berkano

Tarot: *Major Arcana:* The Lovers, The Star *Minor Arcana:* Nine of Wands, Nine of Cups, Nine of Pentacles, Nine of Swords

Botanicals: Allspice, Dandelion, Willow, Ginseng, Ivy, House Leek

Crystals & Stones: Alexandrite, Sunstone, Kyanite, Selenite, Pearl

Deities: Brân, Kvasir, Chaos, Arawn, Antenociticus, Min

Exercise: Create a few formulas of oil blends for each of the elements. Keep your ingredients list short by limiting yourself to just three oils for each formula. **Fire Oil Recipe Example:** For a fire oil you might include frankincense, atlas cedar, and juniper. The ratio you need for your recipe is a matter of taste and potency of each oil's fragrance. For this example, start with **4 parts frankincense, 1 part juniper, and 1 part atlas cedar**. Then adjust the quantities as desired for fragrance. Below are a few oils and their element associations. Some oils are associated with more than one element. Visit the link to expand your study of these and other oils.

Elemental Oil Correspondences

Fire: Basil, Cedarwood, Clove, Frankincense, Juniper, most Citrus oils, Peppermint, Rosemary, Rose Geranium

Water: Spearmint, Eucalyptus, Jasmine, Lemon, Myrrh, Sandalwood, Spearmint, Ylang-Ylang, Lotus

Earth: Oakmoss, Myrrh, Cypress, Wormwood, Vetiver, Patchouli

Air: Lavender, Anise, Lemongrass, Pine, Sage, Peppermint

More Information: PracticalWitch.com/September

September

1
2
3
4
5
6 New
7
8
9
10
11
12
13 First Quarter
14
15
16
17
18
19
20 Full
21
22 ⊕ Equinox Sabbat 2:21 pm
23
24
25
26
27
28 Last Quarter
29
30
31

Natural Lotion Recipe

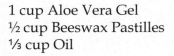

1 cup Aloe Vera Gel   3 tbl. Plant Butter
½ cup Beeswax Pastilles   1 tsp. Vitamin E Oil
⅓ cup Oil   15 drops Essential oil

Remember the mayonnaise recipe from page 92. This lotion is the next step in learning about brewing up potions with oil and water. The oil you choose for your lotion can be apricot, almond, avocado, grapeseed, hemp, jojoba, olive, or other high-quality oil. You can also use any combination of these oils. The plant butter is optional and if you wish to add it use shea butter, cocoa butter, avocado butter, mango butter, or any combination of these.

Instead of using fancy emulsifying waxes (polysorbate-60) or other emulsifiers or preservatives, this recipe uses pre-made aloe vera gel that is readily available at most pharmacies. Although this type of gel usually contains some preservatives (natural or otherwise), preservatives normally function through ratios. Since you will be adding more oils and waxes to the gel, it will not have a very long shelf-life. The Vitamin E will help extend its shelf life, but it is helpful to keep your lotion in the refrigerator or add anti-bacterial essential oils such as rosemary, lavender, or oregano. It should last a month or so under refrigeration. **You can also use essential oils based on their magical properties to make a potion lotion!**

In a glass bowl, combine the Oil, Plant Wax, and Beeswax Pastilles. Heat these oils and waxes in the microwave (or a double boiler), stirring every 30-60 seconds until everything is melted. Be careful not to let it heat over 165°F, which is the maximum heat required to melt most beeswax. Just before the smallest pieces of beeswax pastilles have dissolved, stir the liquid without heating it for a minute to see if they will melt the rest of the way without returning to the microwave or double boiler. Once liquid, set aside the bowl until it cools to around 80°F.

Combine the Aloe Vera Gel, Essential Oils, and Vitamin E. in a food processor or blender. Pulse the mixture briefly and then set the blender to low and *very slowly* drizzle in the liquid oil and wax mixture. Stop occasionally to scrape the sides. It is important to be patient for this step, as it can take 10-15 minutes. When the mixture is thick and consistent, pour it into jars and refrigerate. When cold, your lotion might be a thicker cream-like consistency.

Look inside & express your love.
Color: Purple

Monday 30

◑2:13 am
Mary Wollenstone Shelley's Birthday (author of *Frankenstein*)

Tuesday 31

Raymond Buckland's Birthday

Wednesday 1

☽→♋ 12:26 am
Emma M. Nutt Day[20]

Thursday 2

Friday 3

☽→♌ 10:58 am

Saturday 4

World Sexual Health Day
International Newspaper Carrier Day[21]

Sunday 5

☽→♍ 6:06 pm
Crazy Horse's Birthday

A Guide to Necklace & Chain Lengths

Determine how a necklace length will work for you by considering your neck size, trapezius and platysmu musculature, "Adam's apple" (especially for collars and chokers), chest and bust size.

A and **B**
Collars fit at the most narrow area of the neck.
12-14 inches / 30-36 cm
Chokers are a more relaxed fit, pendants rest on the throat chakra 14-16 inches / 36-41cm

C Prince/Princess length is nice to prevent swing while staying under high collars or outside of low collars. 17-19 inch / 43-49cm

D and **E** or longer, between E and F
Matinee length will land a pendant between the breasts, over the heart chakra, or even to the solar plexus. This is a wide length range overlapping **C** at 19-24 inches / 48-61cm

F Opera length puts most pendants around the solar plexus and naval chakras. 24-35 in/61-89cm

G Rope length reaches naval and root at 35+inch/89+cm

Birth Stones

Birth stones are also known as natal stones. Wearing the stone that corresponds with your birth month is supposed to help you think more clearly and keep your inner calm, harmonize your chakras, and manifest your magic more easily. From a practical perspective, they definitely encourage you to learn about stones.

January: Garnet
February: Amethyst, Pearl, Hyacinth
March: Bloodstone, Jasper, Aquamarine
April: Diamond, Sapphire, Quartz Crystal
May: Emerald, Agate, Chryoprase
June: Cat's Eye, Turquoise, Agate, Pearl, Moonstoone, Alexandrite
July: Turquoise, Onyx, Ruby, Carnelian
August: Sardonyx, Carnelian, Moonstone, Topaz, Peridot, Spinel
September: Chrysolite, Sapphire, Lapis Lazuli
October: Opal, Aquamarine, Tourmaline
November: Topaz, Pearl, Citrine
December: Bloodstone, Ruby, Turquoise, Lapis Lazuli, Zircon, Tanzanite

Finances are stable in the long run.
Color: Gray

Monday 6

● ♍ 7:51 pm
Labor Day (U.S. Federal) & Labour Day (Canadian National)

Tuesday 7

☽→♎ 10:21 pm
Independence Day (Brazil)

Wednesday 8

International Literacy Day

Thursday 9

Friday 10

☽→♏ 1:05 am
Carl Llewelyn Weschcke's Birthday

Saturday 11

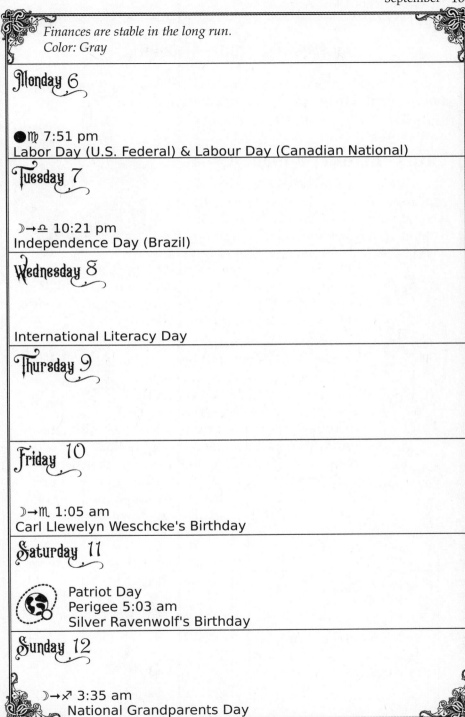

Patriot Day
Perigee 5:03 am
Silver Ravenwolf's Birthday

Sunday 12

☽→♐ 3:35 am
National Grandparents Day

Crafting Your Clothing

Try these simple ideas to make a cape, cloak, or poncho that makes you feel magical. As the weather cools, a flowing fabric draped over your shoulders will keep you warm and Witchy.

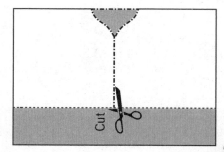

Throw-Blanket Poncho/Cloak

Choose a throw-blanket that speaks to your inner Witch. Cut edges will need to be hemmed to prevent fraying. If you dont want to do any sewing, select a high-quality fleece material that doesn't run. There are also ultra-suede fabrics available that make great sew-free cloaks. If a short length of hemming doesn't scare you off, you can use any material such as a wide scarf or even a table runner.

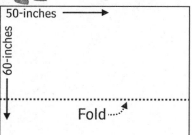

Most throw-blankets measure about 50 inches by 60 inches, more or less. For a pull-over style poncho, fold the throw in half and cut a half circle through both layers along the folded edge to make a neck hole. The pattern diagrams below show a high-low style cloak that will hang down 25 inches in the front and 35 inches in the back. For this style, cuts are made only in the top layer of fabric. Cut down the center and shape a neck hole as desired.

50-inches

60-inches

Fold

Cut

Follow traditions.
Color: Yellow

Monday 13

☾3:39 pm
International Programmer's Day[22]

Tuesday 14

☾→♑ 6:34 am
Neptune at Opposition

Wednesday 15

Make a Hat Day

Thursday 16

☾→♒ 10:23 am
World Ozone Layer Day
Independence Day (Mexico)

Friday 17

Constitution Day and Citizenship Day
National POW/MIA Recognition Day

Saturday 18

☾→♓ 3:23 pm
National Clean-Up Day

Sunday 19

Talk Like a Pirate Day | Cecil Hugh Williamson's Born

Mabon Sabbat

Mabon is also known as Harvest Home and is the second of three harvest Sabbats (Lammas, Mabon, and Samhain). This is an Equinox Sabbat when day and night are almost equal in length. Witches express their gratitude for the successes they've had this year. This can be a success in any area from gardening to facing personal challenges or achieving goals. Autumn leaves, acorns, and seasonal fruits and vegetables adorn many altars. Blessings are made for the winter months, and magic crackles in the air.

Some Witches in the Southern Hemisphere may be celebrating spring this week where it is the Vernal Equinox (Ostara). See page 26 for Southern Hemisphere Sabbats and page 40 for Ostara.

There is an interesting phenomenon that can only be demonstrated twice a year on the Equinox Sabbats when it is sunny outside. These two days are the only times that the Earth's axis is not tilted toward or away from the Sun. This makes it so there is no shadow cast by a stick put into the ground at 90 degrees from the sun. To calculate that 90° in your location, just look up your latitude and subtract it from 90. Then put a stick in the ground at that angle and **the stick won't cast a shadow**! The end of the stick should point towards the Sun. In the Northern Hemisphere this is south, and in the Southern Hemisphere, this is North.

Pictured below I've drawn a drumstick and indicated the angle a stick is put into the ground at the latitude of the Practical Witch sanctuary (at 34.68° latitude). Use a protractor to help you find the exact angle such as 55.32° for the sanctuary (90-34.68). On page 122 there is a diagram of the position of the Earth at each of the eight Sabbats of the Wheel of the Year. You might enjoy visualizing our position on this Sabbat.

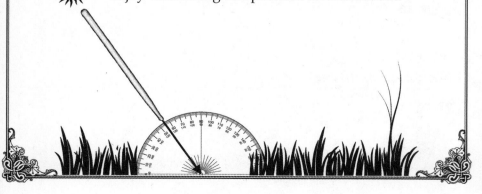

Stability & Firm Foundations
Color: Cobalt Blue

Monday 20

☽→♈ 10:13 pm
○⚹ 6:54 pm
Respect for the Aged Day (Japan)

Tuesday 21

International Day of Peace

Wednesday 22

Equinox Sabbat: Mabon/Ostara (☉→♎ 2:21 pm)

Thursday 23

☽→♉ 7:38 am

Friday 24

T. Thorn Coyle's Birthday

Saturday 25

☽→♊ 7:37 pm

Sunday 26

☿℞ 11:04 pm
Apogee 4:43 pm

October Overview

October is Domestic Violence Awareness Month, Breast Cancer Awareness Month, Diversity Awareness Month, and Black History Month (UK).

Study Guide

Runes: ᛗ Ehwaz, ᛗ Mannaz

Tarot: *Major Arcana:* The Moon, The Sun *Minor Arcana:* Ten of Wands, Ten of Cups, Ten of Pentacles, Ten of Swords

Botanicals: Angelica, Calendula, Comfrey, Dill, High John the Conqueror (Root), Lemongrass

Crystals & Stones: Opal, Amber, Jet, Coral, Abalone & Paua

Deities: Ód, Aphrodite, Camulus, Arnemetia, Jarilo, Manabozho

Exercise: This magical time of the year is perfect for exploring your psychic skills and practicing divination. Page 116 begins an article about Zener cards, a tool to help test and develop your psychic abilities. For your exercises this month, try some forms of divination such as using a pendulum, reading tarot cards, or casting some runes. Give the Zener cards a try either on your own or with a friend. Check out some of the "omancies" on page 86 to inspire you with more ideas about types of of divination.

The Magic of Shells

Shells are used for many forms of magical practice. Cowrie shells such as the one pictured are the type most often used for divination with shells (conchomancy), a practice that originated in Africa and India. You can also make a set of runes with shells. A wonderful water spell can be cast by writing your goal on a shell and throwing it back into the water as you release your intent. You can also carry the inscribed shell with you as a charm. Shells are associated with water, the sea, psychic powers, the divine feminine, birth, and rebirth.

More Information: PracticalWitch.com/October

October

1

2

3

4

5

6 New

7

8

9

10

11

12 First Quarter

13

14

15

16

17

18

19

20 Full

21

22

23

24

25

26

27

28 Last Quarter

29

30

31 ⊛ Sabbat

Liquid Measurement Conversions

CUP (c)	FLUID OUNCE (oz)	TABLESPOON (Tbl.) TEASPOON (tsp) DROPS (gtt)	PINT (pt) QUART (qt)	MILLILITER (mL) GALLON (gal) and LITER (L)
		1/4 tsp		1 mL
		1/2 tsp OR 30 gtt		2 mL
	1/6 oz	1 tsp OR 60 gtt		Appx. 5 mL
	1/2 oz	1 Tbl OR 3 tsp		Appx. 15 mL
1/8 c	1 oz	2 Tbl OR 6 tsp		Appx. 30 mL
1/4 c	2 oz	4 Tbl OR 12 tsp		Appx. 60 mL
1/3 c	3 oz	5 Tbl + 1 tsp		Appx. 90 mL
3/8 c		1/4 c + 2 Tbl		
1/2 c	4 oz	8 Tbl OR 24 tsp		Appx. 125 mL
2/3 c	5 oz	10 Tbl + 2 tsp	1/4 pt	Appx. 150 mL
5/8 c		1/2 Cup + 2 Tbl		
3/4 c	6 oz	12 Tbl		Appx. 200 mL
1 c	8 oz	16 Tbl	1/2 pt OR 1/4 qt	Appx. 250 mL
2 c	16 oz	32 Tbl	1 pt OR 1/2 qt	Appx. 500 mL
4 c	32 oz		2 pt OR 1 qt	1 L OR 1/4 gal
8 c	64 oz		4 pt OR 2 qt	1/2 gal
16 c	128 oz		8 pt OR 4 qt	1 gal OR 3.8 L

Essential oils are sometimes sold in dram vials. One dram is about 3.7 ml or about 56 drops.

Color Correspondences

Red: Lust, Passion, Love, Sexuality, Vigor, Magnetic, Virility
Pink: Unconditional Love, Self Love, Beauty, Love, Friendship
Orange: Courage, Potency, Invigoration, Stimulation, Stamina
Yellow: Intellectual Stimulation, Warmth, General Attraction
Green: Fertility, Jealousy & Envy, Growth, Luck
Light Blue: Healing, Soothing, Peace, Spirituality, Devotion
Dark Blue & Indigo: Psychic Enhancement, Intuition, Wisdom
Violet: Connection to the Divine, Spirituality, Distinction, Expansion, Magic, Influencing Others
Black: Absorbs, Banishing, Reversing Spells, Negativity, Grounding, Protection
White: Protection, General Use, Peace, Purity, Tranquility
Brown: Earth energy, Animals & Familiars, Grounding
Silver: The Moon, Feminine Principle, Clairvoyance
Gold: The Sun, Masculine Principle, Wealth

Delays & Waiting
Color: Lilac

Monday 27

World Tourism Day

Tuesday 28

☽8:57 pm
☽→♋ 8:35 am

Wednesday 29

World Heart Day

Thursday 30

☽→♌ 7:54 pm
National Mud Pack Day
National Hot Mulled Cider Day

Friday 1

World Vegetarian Day
International Coffee Day
Isaac Bonewit's Birthday

Saturday 2

Mahatma Gandhi's Birthday
Gandhi Jayanti (Public holiday in India)

Sunday 3

☽→♍ 3:38 am
Day of German Unity
Daylight Saving Time begins in Australia

Zener Cards for Psychic Growth

Zener cards were developed through a collaboration of Dr. Karl Zener (from Duke University) and J.B. Rhine (a Harvard biologist) in the late 1920s, and have been used in parapsychology experiments. There are five different symbols in a Zener Card Deck as pictured, and five cards of each symbol for a total of 25 cards per deck. You can draw these symbols on index cards to make your deck.

Traditionally, two people use a deck of Zener cards. One person shuffles the deck (the sender) and focuses on each card for a few moments. The second person (the receiver) says which symbol they sense the sender is focusing on. Usually, the receiver is visually separated from the sender, perhaps in another room or building. I have found that it works well to sit on the floor on opposite sides of a closed door.

When two people use a Zener deck, it is an exercise in **telepathy** or "mind-reading". Telepathy literally translates to "distance feeling" and it means to pick up on the thoughts of others. You may find that you are a good "sender" and your friend is a good "receiver" or vice-versa. Knowing your skills will help you customize spells to suit your strengths.

If you are using a Zener deck alone, you are most likely exercising your **precognitive skills**. If there is no "sender" then you are technically "predicting" which card will appear next. This might also be considered **remote viewing** because the order of the cards is set when you shuffle and isn't necessarily in the future. Regardless of what term you use, Zener cards can be a useful tool for testing and exercising your psychic skills.

Continued on page 114

Follow through.
Color: Blue

Monday 4

Child Health Day

Tuesday 5

☽→♎ 7:41 am
World Teacher's Day

Wednesday 6

●♎ 6:05 am

Thursday 7

☄ Draconids
☽→♏ 9:22 am
Arnold Crowther's Birthday

Friday 8

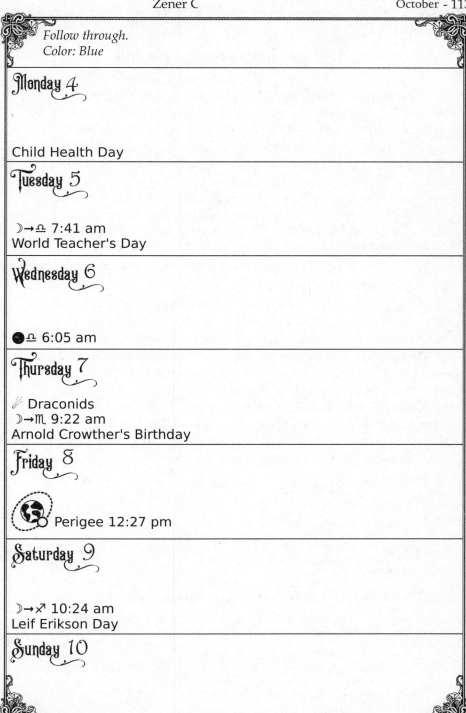 Perigee 12:27 pm

Saturday 9

☽→♐ 10:24 am
Leif Erikson Day

Sunday 10

Continued from page 112

Using Your Zener Cards

Sit in a quiet room out of direct view of your partner and shuffle the cards well. Place the deck face down in front you and selects a card off the top of the deck, focusing on it for about 15 seconds. The receiver calls out the name of the symbol they have guessed (first impulses are usually the most accurate, don't over-think it). You then record the actual card on a chart, along with the guess made by the receiver. The sample worksheet below is a good way to keep records and score easily. The sender should not speak to prevent inadvertently give clues through vocal fluctuations. Repeat this process until all 25 cards have been drawn. If you have three people, one person can record data while the other two send and receive.

A 20% score is average (5 correct guesses). This score can be attributed to chance (1 in 5 chance). Anything above 20% (more than 5 correct) may show potential psychic skills. Anything below 20% (fewer than 5 correct) may also show potential psychic skills! Some people may guess the incorrect answer more often than can be attributed to chance. This "Reverse Psychicism" is an unusual phenomenon that should be identified and corrected whenever it is detected to improve your psychic and magical workings. It indicates great potential, but possible second-guessing. Remember, scores above or below 5 may indicate psychic potential.

0-4=Reverse Psychicism | 5=Average | 6+=Above Average

Date_____ Time_____ Moon Phase, Weather, Mood_____

Sender's Name_____ Receiver_____ Recorder_____

#	Actual Card	Guessed Card	Correct
1			
2			
3			
22			
23			
24			
25			
		Score	

Ask for what you need.
Color: Purple

Monday 11

☽→♑ 12:15 pm
Sports Day (Japan)
Indigenous Peoples' Day
Columbus Day (U.S. Federal) | Thanksgiving Day (Canada)

Tuesday 12

◑10:25 pm
Farmers Day
Our Lady of Aparecida / Children's Day (Brazil)

Wednesday 13

☽→♒ 3:48 pm

Thursday 14

Patricia Crowther's Birthday

Friday 15

☽→♓ 9:22 pm
International Day of Rural Women
Boss's Day | White Cane Safety Day

Saturday 16

Sweetest Day
World Food Day
International Observe the Moon Night

Sunday 17

Meteor Showers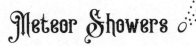

Catch a meteor shower to see some shooting stars this year. Some showers produce bright and colorful shooters such as the Geminids, while others leave long-lasting trails behind them like the Lyrids and Eta Aquarids. Not to be outdone, the Quadrantids might treat you to dazzling fire-balls. If you can't identify constellations just look to the North and North-East sky if you are in the Northern Hemisphere (NH) and to the South if you are in the Southern Hemisphere (SH). m/h=meteors expected per hour on the dates provided.

January 2nd & 3rd - Quadrantids: 40m/h - meteors appear near the North Star. Best viewing in the NH

April 22nd & 23rd - Lyrids: 20m/h - The light of the nearly Full Moon may hinder viewing but this improves after midnight.

May 6th & 7th - Eta Aquarids: 5-10m/h - near the constellation Aquarius in the East after midnight. Best viewing in the SH. These meteors are the result of dust left behind by Halley's comet.

July 28th & 29th - Delta Aquarids: 15m/h - radiating out of the constellation Aquarius in the East. The Moon will be about 66% full and may hinder viewing.

August 12th & 13th - Perseids: 60m/h - Radiating out of the constellation Perseus, these meteors are the result of the comet Swift-Tuttle's tail. Best viewing an hour or so after the Moon sets at 10:58 pm.

October 7th - Draconids: 10m/h - Best viewing in the early evening after sunset at around 7 pm and before midnight.

October 21st & 22nd - Orionids: 25m/h - Moonlight will be too bright for best viewing but some bright shooters may shine through after midnight.

November 4th & 5th -Taurids: 5-10m/h - radiating from the constellation Taurus. Coinciding with the New Moon, the Taurids should be easy to spot.

November 17th & 18th - Leonids: 15m/h - Radiating from the constellation Leo, these meteors occur when Earth passes through the dust from comet Tempel-Tuttle. A bright Moon this year will obscure most meteors.

December 13th & 14th - Geminids: 70m/h – This should be a good year to view the Geminids with the moon at only 1% full. Shower radiates from the constellation Gemini. The moon will be bright but Geminid meteors are so plentiful that they compete well with the moonlight. The Moon sets just after 2 am and the best viewing will be an hour or two after that.

December 21st & 22nd - Ursids: 5-10m/h - Not the best year for this shower that in the past has had over 80m/h. Look towards the constellation Ursa Minor (the little dipper).

Generosity
Color: Pale Yellow

Monday 18

☽→♈ 5:04 am
☿ Direct 10:07 am

Tuesday 19

Wednesday 20

☽→♉ 2:59 pm
○♈ 9:56 am
Selena Fox's Birthday

Thursday 21

☄ Orionids

Friday 22

☄ Orionids
☉→♏ 11:52 pm

Saturday 23

☽→♊ 2:58 am
Gertrude Ederle's Birthday (first woman to swim the English Channel)

Sunday 24

Apogee 10:28 am
United Nations Day

Samhain Sabbat

One of the most beloved Sabbats, Samhain is a time of bobbing for apples, adorning altars with harvest foods and colorful autumn leaves, carving pumpkins or turnips[23], hosting silent suppers[24], or dancing around ritual fires. For some Witches, Samhain marks the beginning of the New Year[25]. On the opposite side of the world, Beltane is being celebrated (see page 56). These two Sabbats are honored by nearly all Witches, and both Sabbats are extremely popular. Because they are so popular, there is an abundance of information about them and nearly all books and articles mention that the *veil between the worlds* is thin at this time.

The veil is a metaphor for the intangible edge of reality sometimes perceived as a mist, gossamer, or hedge. It separates the magical from the mundane, the spiritual from the material, the subconscious from the conscious.

As we head into the winter months we instinctively begin to think about death. For most of human history, this was a time when the sick or weak, the very young, or the very old would not make it through harsh winters when food was scarce. This is also the time of year when herds and flocks were culled to conserve grain stores and provide meat for the coming months. Samhain is both a thanksgiving of the bounty of harvest, and a time when we reflect upon our own mortality. We understand that life is dependent upon death, we honor the dead and our ancestors, and we face our inner shadows to find balance and harmony within ourselves.

This meditation on death is not only instinctual and subconscious. The veil waivers at certain Sabbats like Beltane and Midsummer, but most especially on Samhain. Because of this, is easier to move between the worlds, use our psychic powers, commune with the dead, or delve into our subconscious motivations.

The veil also separates reality from potential, and when you are inside a properly cast Witch's Circle you are between the worlds in a way that is similar to the energy of Sabbats. In the circle, you are in place-that-is-not-a-place, and at a time-beyond-time. When we perform magic during times of the year when the veil is thin, it is even easier to manifest our desires. These are also times that vibrate with magical energy and Witches feel this power. We tap into this extra energy to cast spells or perform rituals, and especially to practice divination. Consider trying your hand at some form of divination or play around with your Zener cards for Samhain this year!

Moderation, patience, compromise.
Color: Lavender

Monday 25

☽→♋ 4:01 pm
World Pasta Day
International Artist Day
Labour Day (New Zealand)

Tuesday 26

National Pumpkin Day

Wednesday 27

National Black Cat Day

Thursday 28

◑3:05 pm
☽→♌ 4:08 am

Friday 29

Hermit Day

Saturday 30

☽→♍ 1:10 pm
National Candy Corn Day

Sunday 31

Halloween
Sabbat: Samhain/Beltane
Daylight Saving Time ends in the UK & Germany

November Overview

November is Native American Heritage Month, Epilepsy Month, Diabetes Awareness Month, National Adoption Awareness Month, and Caregivers Appreciation Month.

Study Guide

Runes: ᛚ Laguz, ◊ Ingwaz

Tarot: *Major Arcana:* Judgment *Minor Arcana:* Page of Wands, Page of Cups, Page of Pentacles, Page of Swords, Knight of Wands, Knight of Cups, Knight of Pentacles, Knight of Swords

Botanicals: Caraway, Marjoram, Nutmeg, Mandrake, Cayenne

Color: Green

Crystals & Stones: Bloodstone, Moss Agate, Carnelian, Fire Opal

Deities: Ra, Hades, Rhiannon, Hecate (Hekate), Gitche Manitou, Pele

Exercise: An extremely effective way of improving your visualization skills is to listen to stories. While listening to audiobooks or storytellers, you must build an entire world in your mind. This is very similar to the visualization necessary to *see* your magical goals when casting spells.

When you cast a spell, you are *choosing* your path out of an infinite array of possibilities. To make that probability a reality, you must *see* your goal as if it is already manifest. Reading fiction is also effective however, listening to stories will target specific areas of the mind that will help you develop magical skills a little faster. Whether you read fiction or listen to recordings, you'll be developing important skills. Videos feed you the visual input, and after years of watching instead of listening, it can be difficult to get into a story that's told instead of shown. Be persistent and try 15-minutes sessions at a time if you have trouble concentrating.

There are many free videos online of authors reading their books aloud. When you listen to these, remember to practice your visualization and don't multitask on your device.

More Information: PracticalWitch.com/November

November

1 ⊕ Sabbat
2
3
4 New
5
6 ⊕ Exact Cross-Quarter 10:50 pm
7
8
9
10
11 First Quarter
12
13
14
15
16
17
18
19 Full
20
21
22
23
24
25
26
27 Last Quarter
28
29
30
31

Sabbats & Exact Cross-Quarters

To find the exact times of your Sabbats, select your time zone from the top row of the table on page 128. If your zone is not listed, use the Time Zone Conversion information on page 12.

What are Quarters & Cross Quarters:

Quarters are the Equinox and Solstice Sabbats (two of each). The Cross-Quarter Sabbats traditionally fall on these dates:

Imbolc - February 2

Beltane - May 1

Lughnasadh - August 1

Samhain - November 1.

Celebrations usually begin at sunset on the evening before the Sabbat date. However, it is now possible to calculate the exact midway point between the Quarters in degrees along the Earth's orbit around the Sun. Modern Witches may begin celebrations the evening before the traditional date as usual, but may continue activities and celebrations through to the exact Cross-Quarter date.

In the image below you can see that the exact Cross-Quarters are more precise than simply dividing the calendar days between Solstices and Equinoxes. After all, a quarter is one forth, and a fourth of a circle is 90°. Exact Cross-Quarters fall 90° apart as do the Solstices and Equinoxes. Sabbat falls 45° along the ecliptic from the next Sabbat. Traditional Cross Quarters dates are marked with ✖ and you can see that they fall slightly before the 45° spacial distance of the exact Cross-Quarter dates.

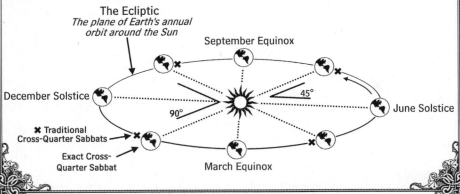

The Ecliptic
The plane of Earth's annual orbit around the Sun

September Equinox

December Solstice

45°

June Solstice

90°

✖ Traditional Cross-Quarter Sabbats

Exact Cross-Quarter Sabbat

March Equinox

Leaving the past behind.
Color: White

Monday 1

☽→♎ 6:11 pm
Day of the Dead
National Author's Day
World Vegan Day

Tuesday 2

Election Day
All Souls' Day

Wednesday 3

☽→♏ 7:53 pm
Sandwich Day
Culture Day (Japan)

Thursday 4

⁘ Taurids
●♏ 4:14 pm

Friday 5

⁘ Taurids
☽→♐ 7:53 pm
Perigee 5:17 pm
National Love Your Red Hair Day | Guy Fawkes Day/Night

Saturday 6

Sabbat: Cross Quarter 10:50 pm (Sun at 15° ♏)

Sunday 7

☽→♑ 7:04 pm
Daylight Saving Time ends 2:00 am
Set Clocks back -1 hour (U.S.) | New York City Marathon

Sabbats & Exact Cross Quarters

Times in 24 hour format: Noon = 12:00, Midnight = 24:00

Festival (Northern) — [Southern: Perth/New Zealand]	Hawaii	Alaska	Pacific	Mountain	Central	Eastern	Atlantic	GMT	Central Europe	Perth	New Zealand
Imbolc: February 3 — [Lughnasadh: August 7]	04:40	05:40	06:40	07:40	08:40	09:40	10:40	14:40	15:40	14:53	18:53
Ostara: March 20 — [Mabon: September 23]	23:37	🕐01:37	🕐02:37	🕐03:37	🕐04:37	🕐05:37	🕐06:37	09:37	10:37	03:21	07:21
Beltane: May 4 — [Samhain: November 7]	20:36	🕐22:36	🕐23:36	🕐00:36	🕐01:36	🕐02:36	🕐03:36	06:36	🕐08:36	12:50	🕐17:50
Midsummer: June 20 — [Yule: Dec. 21 / Dec. 22]	17:32	🕐19:32	🕐20:32	🕐21:32	🕐22:32	🕐23:32	🕐00:32	03:32	🕐05:32	23:59	🕐04:59
Lughnasadh: August 6 — [Imbolc: Feb. 3 / Feb. 4]	20:53	🕐22:53	🕐23:53	🕐00:53	🕐01:53	🕐02:53	🕐03:53	06:53	🕐08:53	22:40	🕐03:40
Mabon: September 22 — [Ostara: March 20]	09:21	🕐11:21	🕐12:21	🕐13:21	🕐14:21	🕐15:21	🕐16:21	19:21	🕐21:21	17:37	🕐22:37
Samhain: November 6 — [Beltane: May 5]	18:50	19:50	20:50	21:50	22:50	23:50	00:50	04:50	05:50	14:36	18:36
Yule: December 21 — [Midsummer: June 21]	05:59	06:59	07:59	08:59	09:59	10:59	11:59	15:59	16:59	11:32	15:32

🕐 Indicates that Daylight Savings Time is in effect and is already calculated into the times provided.

Get involved.
Color: Orange

Monday 8

National Cappuccino Day

Tuesday 9

☽→♒ 9:03 pm
World Freedom Day

Wednesday 10

World Science Day for Peace and Development

Thursday 11

☽6:45 am
Remembrance Day (Canadian)
Veterans Day (U.S. Federal)

Friday 12

☽→♓ 1:54 am

Saturday 13

World Kindness Day

Sunday 14

☽→♈ 9:48 am
National Pickle Day

Elder Futhark Runes

The Elder Futhark is used for divination, magic, and personal reflection. They can be used to inscribe tools or to develop sigils and bind-runes for magic. It is best to develop a good understanding of the runes before such uses, and utilizing them as a divination tool will help you gain the necessary insight. Next to each rune below is its name and English letter equivalent (transliteration), followed by an approximate pronunciation and a summary of each rune's meaning.

ᚠ	F	Fehu /fay-who/ Controlled power over wealth. Manifesting creative energy and power. Invest wisely to increase wealth
ᚢ	U	Uruz /oo-rooz/ Vital strength, primal power, determination health, perseverance, manifestation, wisdom & lore
ᚦ	TH þ	Thurisaz /thoor-ee-sahs/ Thorn, protection, fence, barrier, enemy of baneful forces, defense, destruction, applied power
ᚨ	A	Ansuz /ahn-sooz/ Breath, word/song, incantations, shaping power or sound, expression, communication
ᚱ	R	Raidho /rye-thoh/ Riding, wheel, journey and travel, quest, change, ritual, rhythm, movement, order, the underworld
ᚲ	K	Kenaz /kane-ahz/ Torch, light, fires of transformation, passion, illumination, regeneration, enlightenment, kinship
ᚷ	G	Gebo /gay-boh/ Gift, exchange of powers, relationships, exchanges, crossing paths or uniting, connections, balance
ᚹ	W or V	Wunjo /woon-yo/ Joy, perfection, shared goals, harmony of like forces, best traits of all combined as a force, happiness
ᚺ	H	Hagalaz /haw-gah-lahs/ Hail, hailstone, disruption, destruction, seed form, moving ice, overcoming hardships
ᚾ	N	Naudhiz /now-theez/ Need, necessity, distress, necessity is the mother of invention, resistance, friction creates fire
ᛁ	I	Isa /ee-sah/ Ice, contraction, stillness, suspension, introspection, restraint, slowed growth (can be beneficial), stagnation
ᛃ	J or Y	Jera /yur-ah/ Harvest, year, season, cycles, the flow of life-death-rebirth, fruition, completion, reaping what you sow

Continued on page 128

Be very clear and direct to avoid misunderstandings.
Color: Yellow

Monday 15

Republic Proclamation Day (Brazil)
Day off for Revolution Day Memorial (Mexico)

Tuesday 16

☽→♉ 8:18 pm
International Day of Tolerance

Wednesday 17

☄Leonids
Israel Regardie's Birthday

Thursday 18

☄Leonids

Friday 19

○♉ 2:57 am
☽→♊ 8:33 am
Partial Lunar Eclipse 3:03 am | World Philosophy Day

Saturday 20

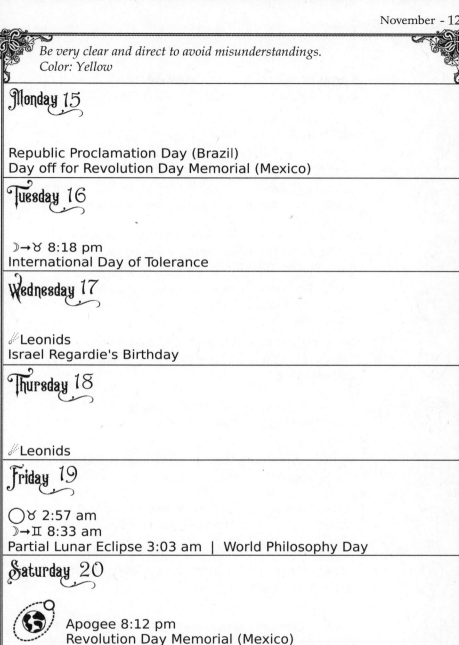

Apogee 8:12 pm
Revolution Day Memorial (Mexico)

Sunday 21

☽→♋ 9:33 pm
☉→♐ 8:34 pm
World Hello Day | World Television Day

Continued from page 126

ᛇ	E ï (æ)	Eihwaz /ii-wahz/ Yew tree, the axis of worlds, endings & beginnings, opportunities, passages, between, protection
ᛈ	P	Perthro /pear-throh/ Dice cup, vulva, birth, problem-solving, evolutionary force, "buy your ticket-you take your ride"
ᛉ	Z	Elhaz /ale-hawz/ or /all-geese/ Elk, protection, defense, support, luck, shielding, sanctuary, connection with deity
ᛊ	S	Sowilo /soh-wil-oh/ or /so-woo-loh/ Sun, will, strength, victory, success, vitality, healing, solar energy and movement, directing power, clarity
ᛏ	T	Tiwaz /tee-wahz/ Creator, justice, success, responsibility, will, guided to success-truth-victory-justice-a good path, law & order
ᛒ	B	Berkano /bear-kahn-oh/ Birch tree, birch twig, life-death-rebirth, regeneration, growth, intuition, female fertility, new beginnings
ᛖ	E	Ehwaz /ay-wahz/ or /ay-woh/ Horse, movement, connections, connecting with another force to move toward a goal
ᛗ	M	Mannaz /mahn-nahz/ Man (human), exams, disputes, challenges, arguments, gaining an upper hand, communication.
ᛚ	L	Laguz /lah-gooz/ Water, lake, flowing, emotions, intuition, psychic powers, revealing what is hidden (like beneath the water)
ᛝ	NG ŋ	Ingwaz /eeng-wahz/ Fertility, Frey, potential energy, opportunity, how endings affect beginnings
ᛞ	D	Dagaz /thah-gahz/ Day, a new day, new beginning, satisfactory or successful conclusion, positive end, final release.
ᛟ	O	Othala /oath-ah-lah/ Home, sacred ancestral land, inherited land, inheritance, ancestral power, true wealth and treasures.

A blank rune is found in some sets but is not a historical part of the Elder Futhark[26].

Victory. Stress eases.
Color: Sage Green

Monday 22

Go For a Ride Day

Tuesday 23

National Espresso Day
Labor Thanksgiving Day (Japan)

Wednesday 24

☽→♌ 9:50 am

Thursday 25

Thanksgiving Day (U.S. Federal)

Friday 26

☽→♍ 8:12 pm
Black Friday
Buy Nothing Day

Saturday 27

◑ 6:27 am

Sunday 28

National French Toast Day

December Overview

December is Bingo Month and Write to a Friend Month.

Study Guide

Runes: ᛗ Dagaz, ᛟ Othala

Tarot: *Major Arcana:* The World *Minor Arcana:* Queen of Wands, Queen of Cups, Queen of Pentacles, Queen of Swords, King of Wands, King of Cups, King of Pentacles, King of Swords

Botanicals: Parsley, Verbena, Fern, Agrimony, Fennel, Cumin

Crystals & Stones: Sodalite, Zircon, Topaz, Turquoise

Deities: Artemis, Fer Doirich, Aengus, Anubis, Chac, Eingana

Exercise: It is the time of year when we write! From holiday greeting cards to family newsletters, we correspond with our loved ones most often through the written word at this time of the year. Practice your writing skills and explore your creativity by writing in your Book of Shadows, journal, or blog. You might also consider getting some special ritual tools for your Book of Shadows such as a glass ink pen. These are excellent tools for using magical inks like Dragon's Blood, or inks that contain shimmer, ground herbs, or essential oils. They do not clog as readily as fountain pens, and they are easier to use for beginners than quill dip pens. Practice using magical alphabets such as Theban Script (page 78), runes (page 126) or Malachim[27].

Malachim Alphabet

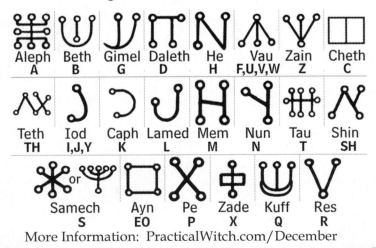

Aleph	Beth	Gimel	Daleth	He	Vau	Zain	Cheth
A	B	G	D	H	F,U,V,W	Z	C

Teth	Iod	Caph	Lamed	Mem	Nun	Tau	Shin
TH	I,J,Y	K	L	M	N	T	SH

Samech	Ayn	Pe	Zade	Kuff	Res
S	EO	P	X	Q	R

More Information: PracticalWitch.com/December

December

1

2

3

4 New

5

6

7

8

9

10 First Quarter

11

12

13

14

15

16

17

18 Full

19

20

21 ✪ Solstice Sabbat 9:59 am

22

23

24

25

26

27

28 Last Quarter

29

30

31

Gluten-Free Peanut Butter Cookies

This is a simple three-ingredient, gluten-free cookie. Mix **1 ½ cup sugar**, **1 egg**, and **8 oz peanut butter**. Form the dough into ping-pong ball size pieces and arrange an inch apart on a cookie sheet. Flatten the balls slightly or leave them to have high centered cookies with soft middles. **Bake for 9-12 minutes at 325°F.** You want them to be just browned, and rather soft in the center. They set up as they cool. Creamy type peanut butter works best rather than the natural types with a layer of oil that has separated at the top of the jar. There are usually some undissolved sugar granule in these cookies, giving them a nice texture. The dough can be frozen into a tube and ½ inch slices can be baked-off when you want a treat. Try mixing in other chopped nuts, dried fruits, or chocolate chips if desired.

Eclipse Cookies

This recipe began with a chocolate craving and a box of Duncan Hines® brownie mix, but any brownie mix will work. Double the recipe above using: **3 cups sugar, 2 eggs, 16 ounces peanut butter**. Add ¼ cup **water**, **1 cup rolled oats**, and ½ **teaspoon salt**. Let this mixture sit for an hour to allow the oats to absorb the liquid. While you wait, make a brownie mix with one less egg than suggested (I use 2 eggs for this mix, 1 egg for Pillsbury® Fudge Brownie mix, etc.). Omit the water and just add the oil indicated on the box. For intense chocolate, add **1 cup chocolate chips** to the brownie mix. Spread the peanut butter dough out on waxed paper and shape the brownie dough into a tube in the middle. Chill for 1 hour, roll the peanut butter dough around the brownie mix. The dough can be frozen or refrigerated and ½ to 1-inch slices can be baked-off when you want a treat. **Bake as above for 9-12 minutes at 325°F or** until browned but still somewhat soft in the center. Allow to cool and set up before removing from the pan.

Speak your mind. Make boundaries.
Color: Black

Monday 29

☽→♎ 2:55 am
Cyber Monday
Chanukah/Hanukkah (first day)
Square Dance Day

Tuesday 30

Witches meet Hecate at the crossroads

Wednesday 1

☽→♏ 5:56 am
Rosa Parks Day (state holiday in Ohio & Oregon)
1st military grave marker with a pentacle allowed for veterans 2007

Thursday 2

Toilet paper roll was patented[28]

Friday 3

☽→♐ 6:13 am

Saturday 4

Super ●♐ 1:43 am
Total Solar Eclipse 1:33 am
International Cookie Day
Perigee 4:03 am (Closest to the Earth in 2021)

Sunday 5

☽→♑ 5:31 am
International Volunteer Day | Repeal Day | World Soil Day
Krampus Night (*Krampusnacht*) *see page 138*

Krampus

Krampus is a horned half-goat creature of European folklore. He is the counterpart to Saint Nicholas so instead of rewarding good children, Krampus punishes those who misbehave.

Since the 1800s, Krampus greeting cards (*Krampuskarten*) have been exchanged such as the one pictured here. There are obvious aspects of these cards with Pagan origins such as the bundle of birch branches (*ruten*) he carries. Birch is a traditional material used in magic and Witches' besoms. He uses the birch bundles to punish children, and this echoes many ancient initiatory rites. He is depicted with a basket he uses to carry evil children away.

Even in modern times, Krampus Eve is celebrated in parts of Europe on the eve of December 5th. Costumed participants roam through settlements visiting homes and shops, distributing birch sticks and coal. Sometimes he is accompanied by Saint Nicholas who distributes gifts.

No-Fail Bath Bombs

This easy bath bomb recipe is just in time for Yule gift-giving. You'll need a small spray bottle filled with rubbing alcohol or witch hazel extract. ❶ Warm **4 tsp. Coconut Oil** until liquid (about 100°F). Stir in ½ **tsp. Essential Oil(s)**. ❷ Add oil mixture to **1 c. Baking Soda** and blend well. This prevents fizzing in your molds or in storage. ❸ In a separate bowl mix ½ **c. Citric Acid** with ¼ **c. Cornstarch or Arrowroot Powder**, then mix into oiled baking soda. ❹ Spray just a little Extract or Alcohol onto the mixture and combine. Continue the spray/combine combo until the mixture just sticks together. Don't over-wet. ❺ Pack into molds and cure 48 hours. Once you are good at making this recipe, double it or try adding color and up to ¼ c. Sea Salt or Epsom Salt. On humid days, use extract/alcohol sparingly, don't use salts and consider using a dehydrator on low for curing.

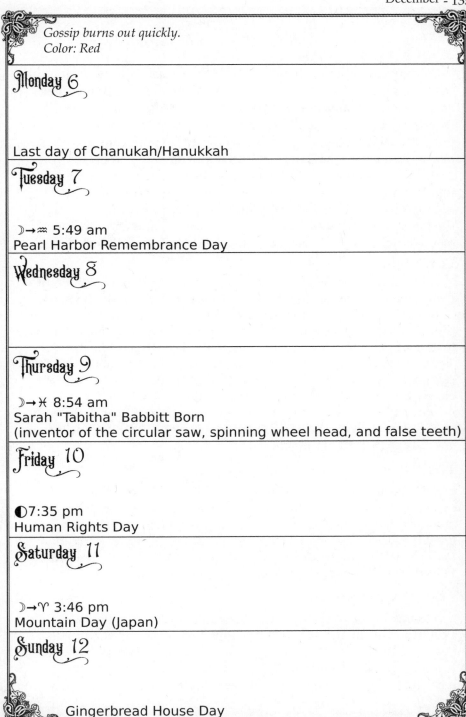

Gossip burns out quickly.
Color: Red

Monday 6

Last day of Chanukah/Hanukkah

Tuesday 7

☽→♒ 5:49 am
Pearl Harbor Remembrance Day

Wednesday 8

Thursday 9

☽→♓ 8:54 am
Sarah "Tabitha" Babbitt Born
(inventor of the circular saw, spinning wheel head, and false teeth)

Friday 10

●7:35 pm
Human Rights Day

Saturday 11

☽→♈ 3:46 pm
Mountain Day (Japan)

Sunday 12

Gingerbread House Day

Witchcraft Traditions

Many paths can be considered "Witchcraft" and here we will cover some of the most common you will encounter[29]. However, before you pick a "label" for yourself consider that you are an ever-evolving individual. That which feeds your spirit now may not suffice later on your path. Consider these paths as always open to you but, I always recommend that you save the labels for your herb cabinet. Like you, Witchcraft is always changing and evolving. Witches incorporate new and old ideas into our practice. This is syncretism. As a syncretic path[30], Witchcraft may incorporate the latest scientific research into wortcunning and shadow work, or use color associations from other cultures for spellwork.

The "Trads"

Different paths of Witchcraft are somewhat similar to different denominations in mainstream religious organizations. These traditions (or "trads") hold specific beliefs and follow specific rituals. Traditions are usually (but not always) religious, meaning that devotion to and worship of a specific deity or deities is central to the practice. Trads are fairly organized structures, usually with an international presence. You can usually contact one **Gardnerian** or **Alexandrian** coven, become initiated, and if you relocate you can reach out to a new coven within your trad at your new location. Other paths with established trads are **British Traditional Wicca** (BTW), **Dianic Wicca**, and **Strega** (Stregheria Witchcraft).

The Paths

Paths are loose terms, referring to the "flavor" or emphasis of an individual's practice. Paths may be religious, secular, agnostic, or anything else. Beliefs and practices vary as widely as the individuals on each path, and some practitioners consider their path a tradition. Path labels include **Hedge Witch**, **Hereditary Witch**, **Kitchen Witch**, **Eclectic Witch**, Hearth Witch, **Green Witch**, and many more.

Trad/Path Hybrids

Some labels refer to either trads and paths such as the **Fairy Witches**. This might refer to someone following a trad such as the Faerie Faith, the Feri Tradition, or Faery Wicca. As a path, Faery or Fairy Wicca is any modern Witchcraft path that emphasizes the Fae (fairy realm of elves, sprites, faeries, etc).

Organize.
Color: Brown

Monday 13

☄Geminids
National Cocoa Day

Tuesday 14

☄Geminids
☽→♉ 2:11 am

Wednesday 15

Bill of Rights Day
Friday Gladheart's Birthday

Thursday 16

☽→♊ 2:43 pm
International Mountain Day

Friday 17

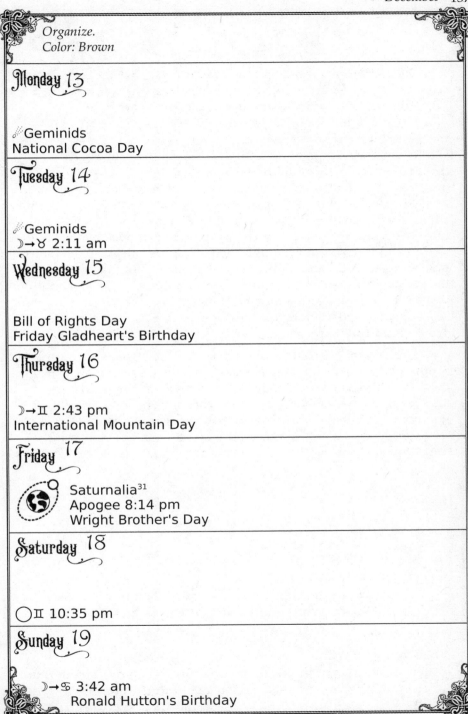

Saturnalia[31]
Apogee 8:14 pm
Wright Brother's Day

Saturday 18

○♊ 10:35 pm

Sunday 19

☽→♋ 3:42 am
Ronald Hutton's Birthday

Yule Sabbat

This is the longest night of the year and the season of darkness in the Northern Hemisphere. This Sabbat is opposite Midsummer on the Wheel of the Year and the opposite side of the world in the Southern Hemisphere. The days have grown shorter since Midsummer up until this, the darkest day. To celebrate the return of the Sun, Witches will turn out all lights and meditate in the darkness, facing their shadows, reflecting deities, and enjoying the stillness that winter brings. A candle or fire is then lit to represent the return of the Sun. Celebrations include decorating with evergreen boughs to symbolize that life holds in wait and is never fully extinguished. Holly, mistletoe, birch twigs, pomegranate, bells, and pine cones adorn altars. Solstice comes from the Latin word *solstitium*, meaning 'Sun stands still'. Like a pendulum that seems to hesitate for a moment between swinging to and fro, the Sun appears to be still for a few moments before it begins its journey southward in our skies again.

The December Solstice occurs when the Sun reaches its most southerly declination and the North Pole is tilted furthest away from the Sun. This brings many long nights and we exchange "winter's tales" with themes of facing personal fears and shadows. Like the Equinoxes and Exact Cross-Quarter Sabbats (pages 126 & 128), Solstices are specific points in time and space. If you are celebrating Midsummer in the Southern Hemisphere right now, see page 72.

Yule Incense

1 part Star Anise
2 parts Myrrh resin
2 parts Frankincense resin
1 part ground Cloves
1 part ground Cinnamon or Cinnamon chips
4 parts White Sandalwood chips

Break up the star anise and resins in your pestle and mortar so they are consistent in size to the sandalwood chips. Mix in the remaining ingredients and use over incense charcoals.

Focus on one challenge at a time, you got this!
Color: Light Blue

Monday 20

Tuesday 21

Ursids
☽→♌ 3:54 pm
Crossword Puzzle Day (see page 142)
Solstice Sabbat: Yule/Midsummer (☉→♑ 9:59 am)

Wednesday 22

Ursids

Thursday 23

Festivus

Friday 24

☽→♍ 2:25 am
Christmas Day observed
(U.S. Federal & Canadian National Holiday)

Saturday 25

Christmas Day

Sunday 26

☽ ●8:23 pm | ☽→♎ 10:24 am
First day of Kwanzaa | Boxing Day
St. Stephen's Day (National Holiday in Ireland)

Connect & Sync

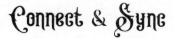

There more goodies for you at the official PractialWitch.com website. Just visit the site and create a free account to login and access these great features. Certain pages are only for owners of The 2021 Practical Witch's Almanac, so you may have to enter a page-password. If you are asked for a page-password, just translate the magical alphabet below (see page 78) and enter it:

- Download a free, printable companion wall calendar that matches your almanac.

- Get print-ready templates, borders, and fonts for your Book of Shadows

- Grab printable tarot cards, Zener cards, rune cards, and psychic worksheets.

- Access correspondence pages with the magical and metaphysical properties for hundreds of herbs, crystals, and stones.

- Look up keywords and interpretations for the tarot and runes, or print a pendulum board to help with your scrying.

- **Sync the data from your almanac with your device's calendar!**

Stay in Touch

Once or twice a month you can receive updates on your device via text message or push notifications. These messages are sent directly from the author and you can reply to Friday Gladheart through the app or text message. Updates include links to bonus features, and free downloads, Sabbat greetings, and other events. Simply send the text message **@almanac** to the number **81010** or get the app by visiting: remind.me/almanac

Communication feeds creativity.
Color: Pink

Monday 27

Tuesday 28

☽→♏ 3:17 pm
National Card Playing Day

Wednesday 29

Pepper Pot Day (Recipe)

Thursday 30

☽→♐ 5:08 pm

Friday 31

New Year's Day (U.S. Federal observed)

Saturday January 1, 2022

☽→♑ 5:02 pm
New Year's Day

Sunday 2

Witchy Crossword Challenge

Across

6. The oil from this plant is used to finish runes, the fibers make linen
7. This Goddess's name means silver wheel
9. Some Witches have 2 bowls on their altars, one for salt and the other for ____.
11. In 1986 the court case Dettmer v. Landon recognized Wicca as a _____.
13. You might see a carved turnip on an altar for this Sabbat.
14. Fungus thought to have triggered the "bewitched" residents in Massachusetts as published in a 1976 study.
17. Author and blogger Mat ____ is a priest in the Sacred Fires Witchcraft tradition
18. A Solar Eclipse can only occur during the ____ Moon phase
20. Pine ____ are used in making pesto.
21. Keys can be her symbols
22. A baneful spell, curse
23. First name of the founder of the Gardnerian tradition
25. The Lady's tree that boosts immunity
26. Lignum ____ is a very oily and dense "wood of life"
27. The color of lapis lazuli
28. Divination with a crystal sphere, mirror, or dark pool.
30. A female magical practitioner may be called this in Spanish
34. A handfasting tradition is to "jump the ____"
36. A male with is called a ____
37. Elemental being associated with Earth. Hint: garden statues
38. Also known as hazelnuts
40. Another name for the Summer Solstice
42. Syncretic Afro-American religion that arose from West African and Roman Catholic traditions
44. Elemental being associated with water
46. The base of the Italian cimaruta magical charm is a branched sprig of this herb.
47. Wiccan baby blessing
49. A Lunar Eclipse can only occur during the ____ Moon phase.
53. Ritual held by Witches on the Full Moon
54. Clockwise
56. Ice rune
57. The penalty for practicing Witchcraft in modern day Saudi Arabia
61. Scientific study of celestial objects
63. Seven major vortices of energy in the human body
64. Egyptian hieroglyphic symbol of life or longevity
66. Color associated with the prosperity and the heart chakra
69. A protection spell used "to turn or bend" away
70. "In perfect ____ and perfect trust."
71. Black lignite coal used as a stone of mourning and protection
72. A vermifuge in wortcunning is used to expel ____
74. "Viking's Compass" stone with pleochroism to help you determine the direction of the sun on overcast days
76. Abbreviation of the calendar era that replaced the monk's AD

Across continued...

79.   It remained in Pandora's box
81.   Number of Wiccan Sabbats (most trads)
86.   Three vesica piscis form this trinity symbol
88.   Pyewacket is a familiar name of a ____ to Witches like Elizabeth Clarke
         or the fictional Gillian Holroyd
89.   Hagalaz rune, frozen rain
92.   The _____ of the Goddess is a story of the message from the Goddess to her children
94.   Major and minor secrets of the tarot
95.   "Cakes and ___" are served at rituals.
96.   Title of a liar, thief, or oath-breaker to Wiccans
86.   Three vesica piscis form this trinity symbol
88.   Pyewacket is a familiar name of a___ to Witches like Elizabeth Clarke
         or the fictional Gillian Holroyd
89.   Hagalaz rune, frozen rain
92.   The _____ of the Goddess is a story of the message from the Goddess to her children
94.   Major and minor secrets of the tarot
95.   "Cakes and ___" are served at rituals.
96.   Title of a liar, thief, or oath-breaker to Wiccans

Down

1.   The ____ Moon is growing in size
4.   Used to burn resins and herbs in a cauldron
5.   Witch's broom
8.   Legend tells us that mandrake should be pulled from the ground by a white ____.
9.   Name of the "Wildman of the Woods" similar to a satyr or faun
10.   Soil activity is high when the Moon is opposite this planet
12.   Ghanaian woman burned alive in 2010 for being a Witch: Ama _____
13.   Italian Witchcraft
15.   Day of the week associted with love magic
16.   Celtic Goddess associated with horses
19.   Greek sky and thunder God
24.   Spring Sabbat also known as Brigid's Day
26.   To perplex, frustrate, irritate
29.   Animated anthropomorphic being created from inanimate matter in Jewish folklore.
31.   Cat's Eye stones get their chatoyancy from this mineral's inclusion
32.   Hindu Mother Goddess of destruction
33.   The sign of the Full Moon when the Sun is in Libra
35.   Ritual knife used to harvest herbs and carve candles
36.   The practice of magical skills, spells, and abilities currently considered to be "supernatural"
38.   How many corners are in a Witch's circle?
39.   The bull of the Zodiac
41.   The last sheaf of this plant in the field at harvest is made into dollies
43.   Used to shift consciousness or open doors, a symbol of Hecate
45.   Spice of love and blessings used in snicker-doodles
47.   Sabbats mark the turning of The ____ of the Year
48. Mid 20th century Witches celebrated four ____ Sabbats: Imbolc, Beltane, Lammas, Samhain.
    50. This God's hound is named Failinis and he is linked to a harvest Sabbat

Down continued...

51. Malocchio refers to the _____ (2 words)
52. Traditional fabric used to protect tarot cards and ritual tools
55. The eye of this salamander was used by Shakespeare's Witches
58. Author ____ Mooney is a traditional Witch
59. This double edged axe is a symbol or royal power and feminine strength
60. Word popularized in the 1850s by Eliphas Lévi that comes from the Greek word meaning "belonging to an inner circle"
62. October's birthstone that is the multi-tool of stones
65. The Russian word for Witch is??? (Ведьмак=Vĕdmák or Vĕdma) meaning "one who ____"
67. Alternate form of Ostara who's name may have influenced the words Easter and estrogen
68. A guideline or advice such as the Wiccan ____
73. Aleister Crowley added the K to this word
75. Fire sign that roars
77. Derived from the Greek word for uterus or womb, thought to be a "female" disorder or demonic possession
78. Northern California's activist Witch author
80. A _____ ritual has no clothes
82. "Blessed ____" is said for the 5-fold kiss or hello/goodbye
83. Term originally from Late Latin for "country-dweller, of the country, non-combatant"
84. Black handled, double edged ritual knife
85. The top point of a pentagram represents _____
87. A tasseomancer might read this camellia's residual leaves
90. This evergreen is associated with Yule, hex removal, and contains toxic taxine alkaloids
91. Germanic God is the namesake of Tuesday
93. In Italy, a jettatore wields the evil ____

Hints & Word Bank

Need some help? Most of the answers to the clues can be found in this Almanac or through the supplemental reading for each month's Study Guide on the official PracticalWitch.com website. An answer key is available on the site, or try using the word bank below for hints.

ALE ANKH ARCANA ARIANRHOD ARIES ASTRONOMY ATHAME AURYN BE BESOM BLUE BOLINE BROOM BRUJA CAT CE CHAKRAS CHARCOAL CHARGE CINNAMON CORN DEATH DEOSIL DOG EIGHT ELDER EOSTRE ERGOT ESBAT ESOTERIC EVILEYE EYE FILBERTS FLAX FOUR FRIDAY FULL GERALD GNOME GOLEM GREATER GREEN HAIL HECATE HEMMAH HEX HOPE HYSTERIA IMBOLC IOLITE ISA JET KALI KEY KNOWS LABRYS LEO LITHA LOVE LUGH MAGICK NEW NEWT NUTS OPAL PAGAN PAN REDE RELIGION RHIANNON RUE RUTILE SAMHAIN SATURN SCRYING SILK SKYCLAD SPIRIT STARHAWK STREGHERIA TAURUS TEA THORN TRIQUETRA TYR UNDINE VEX VITAE VODOU WANING WARD WARLOCK WATER WAXING WHEEL WICCANING WITCH WITCHCRAFT WOODWOSE WORMS YEW ZEUS

The Witch's Puzzler Crossword

Across

2. Name of Zulu Witches in South Africa who protect people against evil
5. Gardner claimed Dorothy _____ initiated him in 1939
8. These Yuletide treats are the only nuts with Vitamin C
9. Wiccan rule of three is the _____ law.
10. The Navajo *yee naaldlooshii* is known in English as a __
12. The practice of gaining insight, prophesy, or connecting seemingly disjointed patterns.
15. 16th century disorder thought to be intermittent periods of insanity caused by the Moon
16. Slang abbreviation for Witchcraft traditions
21. The first of the 5 fold kiss is for the _____ that have brought thee in these ways
23. Village in Colonial America where Witch trials began in 1692
25. One of the seven "Noble" metals, associated with the Moon
26. Direction of the door in old churches built on ancient Pagan sacred sites where those practicing the old ways could enter, and the "devil" would escape during baptisms
27. Earth Zodiac sign, virgin
32. To disinvite, exile or remove negative influences
33. African based folkways practiced in New Orleans
34. "Screaming" root shaped like a person contains tropane alkaloids
35. Beyond natural
36. Twin air sign
39. Quarter Sabbats with long and short days.
42. Stone used for love and passion named for pomegranates
44. The Greek philosopher Empedocles is best known for originating the cosmogonic theory of the four classical _____ which he referred to as "roots".
46. Lughnasadh, Mabon, and Samhain are _____ Sabbats
48. More accurate name of a "voodoo doll"
50. The ___ Rite is sometimes performed by handfasted couples.
52. Goober peas
54. Study of the influence of celestial bodies and positions
55. Mineral variety of gypsum often used for wands, cleansing, protection
58. Alchemist's mercury
59. Infamous hill in Salem, Massachusetts
60. U.S. president who stated that he believed Wicca isn't a "real" religion.
63. The symbol of a 5 pointed star inside a circle.
64. The study of the bumps on the skull
66. The Craft of cultivating, brewing, and using herbs
67. When the Sun is in Capricorn, then the Full Moon that month will be in _____
68. Pagan way of tying the knot, wedding

Down

1. An oneiromancer might interpret your _____
3. Egyptian Goddess of truth, justice, wisdom, and the stars
4. Exam, odd person

Continued on page 148

This year's crossword puzzles have a few flat-out easy clues, along with some serious brain teasers that will get you hitting the books to brush up on your knowledge. There's sure to be something new to learn in these puzzles!

Continued from page 146

Down

6. Caribbean slave accused of Witchcraft in the U.S.
7. Genus of Monkshood or Wolf's-bane
11. A Witch who practices alone
13. Lignum ____ is a very oily and dense "wood of life"
14. Undesirable, negative, or contrary
17. Lizard-like elemental being associated with fire
18. Counter-clockwise
19. Stomach soothing root
20. A group of Witches who practice together
22. Spell book or magical primer
24. Upside down Tarot Cards are ____
25. Chemical in flying ointment herbs, a.k.a. Hyoscine
28. Fishy water sign
29. Muggle in real life, traitor
30. A combination of runes used like a sigil
31. Using a pendulum or branch to find water
32. It's sound is used to clear the air at the beginning or end of a ritual.
37. Aztec feathered serpent God
38. All the Gods of a people considered as a group, also a Roman temple
40. This rover sings happy birthday to himself on Mars
41. Egyptian God of deserts, Osiris's bane
43. Genus of a favorite feline herb
45. Last name of the founder of the Alexandrian tradition
47. Equal Night Sabbat
49. Incense burner
51. Sabbats mark the turning of The ____ of the Year
53. Two accused Saudi Witches were executed by _____ in 2011 and 2012
54. Egyptian God of death and the afterlife
56. Divination by casting lots
57. Animal associated with Ostara, fertility, and spring
61. This Celtic God wears a gray cloak to take out his Hounds of Hell
62. Elemental being associated with air
65. Greek Earth Mother

Hints & Word Bank

ACONITUM ANUBIS ARAWN ASTROLOGY BANEFUL BANISH BEHEADING BELL BINDRUNE BUSH CANCER CENSER CHESTNUTS CLEROMANCY CLUTTERBUCK COVEN COWAN CURIOSITY DIVINATION DOWSING DREAMS ELEMENTS EQUINOX FEET GAIA GALLOWS GARNET GEMINI GINGER GREAT GRIMOIRE HANDFASTING HARVEST LUNACY MAAT MANDRAKE NEPETA NORTH PANTHEON PEANUTS PENTAGRAM PHRENOLOGY PISCES POPPET QUETZALCOATL QUICKSILVER QUIZ RABBIT REVERSED SALAMANDER SALEM SANDERS SANGOMA SCOPOLAMINE SELENITE SET SILVER SKIN-WALKER SOLITARY SOLSTICES SUPERNATURAL SYLPH THREEFOLD TITUBA TRADS VIRGO VITAE VOODOO WHEEL WIDDERSHINS WORTCUNNING

Complete Answer key at PracticalWitch.com

Glossary

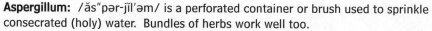

Aspergillum: /ăs"pər-jĭl'əm/ is a perforated container or brush used to sprinkle consecrated (holy) water. Bundles of herbs work well too.

Astronomy: The scientific study of space and celestial objects, and the physical universe.

Athame: A ritual knife used by Witches, usually black handled with a double edged blade.

Bane and Baneful: Bane is anything with an undesirable, contrary, or negative influence. Baneful magic is sometimes called "black magic."

Besom: A broom used for magic and sometimes mundane purposes.

Book of Shadows (BoS): A combination of journal, scrapbook, spells, rituals, recipes, and correspondences (such as your almanac's Directories). Many Witches keep a BoS, either printed or digitally, and they are very useful for keeping track of experiments and developing your personal path.

Deosil: Clockwise movement, also known as *sunwise*.

Cakes & Ale: Traditional meal served at Sabbats and other rituals. A light snack or a meal. Served after the main ritual to help participants ground after expending magical energy or as an integral part of the main ritual with ceremonial blessing and passing of each. What is served as cakes and ale varies widely. Usually the cakes are small sweets like cookies or petit four, and the ale is juice, milk (especially at Imbolc), mead, ale, wine, or potions made of roots and herbs.

Cense: To burn perfume with incense, or to infuse something with incense smoke. Preferred to the culturally appropriated "smudging".

Esbat: A ritual held on the Full Moon, sometimes also on New Moons.

Handfasting: A type of union similar to a marriage.

Knot & Cord Magic: Magic using cords, usually by tying knots to hold a Witch's intentions. This type of magic is especially effective for storing or binding energy to a place or object, or to store energy for later use.

Sabbat: Major festivals, celebrations, and/or holy days celebrated by Witches and many modern Pagans. There are eight Sabbats, the two solstices and two equinoxes (Quarters), and the midpoints in the year between them (Cross-Quarters). The names used for each of the Sabbats, and the number celebrated, vary by tradition.

Tisane: pronounced like *tea's on*, is any tea made from flowers such as chamomile or rose petals.

Votive: A candle used for ritual and devotion, often in a container such as glass.

Widdershins: Counter-clockwise movement

Wortcunning: is the knowledge of the properties of magical and medicinal properties of herbs, plants, and botanicals, the understanding of how to use these natural materials (such as making tinctures, mojo bags, potions, ointments, poultices, etc.) and the wisdom of when and why to use botanicals. "Wort" refers to plants, and cunning refers to cleverness and skill.

Understanding New Moons

New Moons 2021

- ♐ Dec. 4 — 1:43 am
- ♑ Jan. 12 — 11:00 pm
- ♒ Feb. 11 — 1:05 pm
- ♓ Mar. 13 — 4:21 am
- ♈ Apr. 11 — 9:30 pm
- ♉ May 11 — 1:59 pm
- ♊ June 10 — 5:52 am
- ♋ July 9 — 8:16 pm
- ♌ Aug. 8 — 8:49 am
- ♍ Sep. 6 — 7:51 pm
- ♎ Oct. 6 — 6:05 am
- ♏ Nov. 4 — 4:14 pm

The New Moon is *often* in the same Zodiac position as the Sun, or within just a few degrees in an adjoining sign. During a solar eclipse, the New Moon is always in the same sign as the Sun such as occurs on December 4th. A New Moon happens when the Sun is in conjunction to the moon as represented by the astrological abbreviation: ☉ ☌ ☽ = ● New Moon. The illustration below provides a visual understanding of the location of the Moon during a New Moon. As you can see, the Moon is overhead during the daytime when the Moon is new.

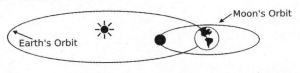

Moon's Orbit

Earth's Orbit

Understanding Full Moons

Full Moons
2021

- ♌ Jan. 28 1:16 pm
- ♍ Feb. 27 2:17 am
- ♎ Mar. 28 1:48 pm
- ♏ Apr. 26 10:31 pm
- ♐ May 26 6:13 am
- ♑ June 24 1:39 pm
- ♒ July 23 9:36 pm
- ♒ Aug. 22 7:01 am
- ♓ Sep. 20 6:54 pm
- ♈ Oct. 20 9:56 am
- ♉ Nov. 19 2:57 am
- ♊ Dec. 18 10:35 pm

The Full Moon is *always* in the opposite sign as the Sun. Astrologers express this as "Moon in opposition" or with the symbols ☉ ☍ ☽ = ◯ Full Moon

Note the Zodiac signs on page 84. On the Solstice of June 20th the Sun enters the sign of Cancer at 10:32 pm. This is when the Sun is at 0° Cancer. If you were to draw a horizontal line straight across from the middle of the Cancer's constellation on the diagram, you'll see that the opposite sign is Capricorn. This shows you that the Full Moon in June will be in Capricorn.

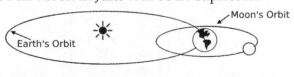

Moon's Orbit

Earth's Orbit

Lunar Eclipses

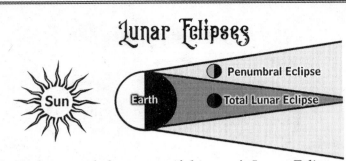

Check the maps below to see if this year's Lunar Eclipses are visible in your area. When the Moon is entirely within the Earth's shadow it is a Total Lunar Eclipse such as on May 26th this year. A Partial Lunar Eclipse such as the one on November 19th occurs when the *umbra* (Latin for *shadow*) appears to take a bite out of a part of the moon. A Penumbral Eclipse (*pen* if from the Latin *pæne* for *nearly* or *almost*) occurs when the diffuse outer shadow of the Earth falls on the Moon's surface. We won't see another Penumbral Eclipse again until May of 2023.

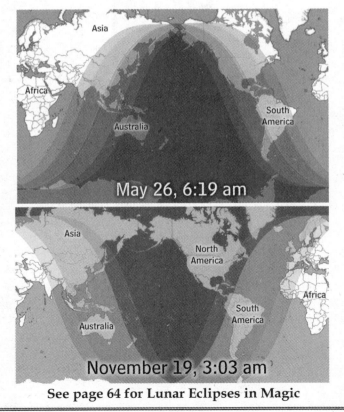

May 26, 6:19 am

November 19, 3:03 am

See page 64 for Lunar Eclipses in Magic

Solar Eclipses

Check the maps below to see if this year's Solar eclipses are visible in your area. The darker the arc on the map, the darker the shadow that's cast on the area. The Annular Solar Eclipse on June 10th will be visible in parts of North America, North-East Asia, and Northern Europe. The Moon is near apogee at this time and because it is farther away from the Earth, it's shadow is smaller, leaving a thin ring of the sun uncovered. The Total Solar Eclipse on December 4th is only visible in Antarctica, with edges of the penumbra in far southern Australia and Africa. The moon is near perigee at this time (close to the Earth) so it will cover the entire face of the Sun. The next Partial Solar Eclipse is April 30,2022.

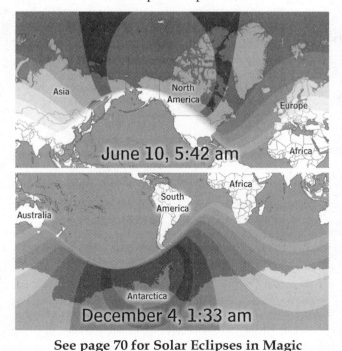

See page 70 for Solar Eclipses in Magic

Yearly Planner

January

February

March

April

May

June

Yearly Planner

July

August

September

October

November

June

Make Your Wheel of the Year

You can customize this Wheel with the names of your Sabbats, and personalize it with other symbols or designs.

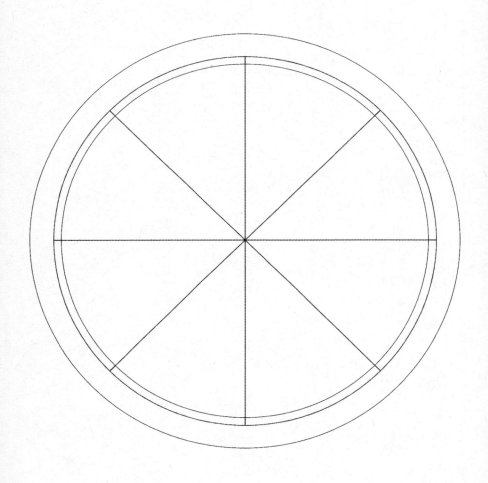

Alphabetical Index

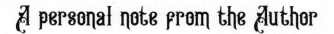

A personal note from the Author

As the end of this year's almanac draws near, I want to thank you for choosing it as your companion for the year. It means more to me than I can express. This year's almanac was part of a Kickstarter project, and if you supported it through the project, a special thanks goes out to you. None of this would be possible without your support.

There is so much to share with all the Practical Witches out there, and it is always difficult to find the end a project. However, as the mayor in the series *Buffy the Vampire Slayer* said in the finale of Season 3, *"I had this whole bit about civic pride, but time's up. Let's cut straight to the end."*

Please stay in touch (page 140), take care of yourself, and have a blessed year! If you color the pages of your almanac or create a Wheel of the Year for yourself (page 156), share them on social media so I can see them with one of the hashtags #PracticalWitch #WitchAlmanac or #PracticalWitchAlmanac

Thank You & Blessed Be!

Endnotes

1   The pin on the map is the location of the sanctuary and teaching garden founded by Friday Gladheart for WitchAcademy.org, home of the oldest online academy for practical magic, Witchcraft, Wicca, herbalism, tarot, and other divinatory arts. A portion of the author's proceeds from the almanac are used to plant trees at this sanctuary every year.

2   When the Moon moves into a sign it is called an ingress. Specifically, an ingress is the moment that the Moon or a planet moves from 29° 59' into a new sign at 0° 0'.

3   Country Peach Passion is a registered trademark of Celestial Seasonings, Inc.

4   The four classical elements as described by the Greek philosopher Empedocles: Earth, Air, Fire, and Water. Aristotle proposed a fifth element, Æther (similar to Akashi in India). Each Element is associated with a cardinal direction (North, East, South, West) and these associations vary by tradition.

5   It is said that some covens in the distant past would "take your measure" before initiation. A cord was used to measure your height and girth and the elders of the coven would keep this cord. This was supposedly a way to enforce secrecy and security during times of persecution. If you broke your oath of secrecy, the coven could potentially use your cord as a magical link to you. *Taking your measure* also implied that the elders were prepared to provide your measurements to the local coffin maker.

6   Salk announced on the radio that he had invented a vaccine to fight polio. He did not patent the vaccine, forfeiting potentially billions for the sake of world health. Thank you Dr. Salk!

7   Up until around 1979 I remember leaving May baskets at all the nearby neighbor houses. This was a sort of "ding-dong-dash" game where you rang the bell and ran away so no one would know who left the basket. This was considered a secular practice, similar to trick-or-treating at Halloween. Into the 80s there was an influx of anti-Pagan propaganda from fundamentalist zealots and this practice quickly fell out of favor in most parts of the Midwest United States.

8   Maypole Dance illustration was adapted from Kate Greenaway's 1879 illustration.

9   A Supermoon occurs when the Full Moon coincides with perigee. The Moon will appear up to 14% larger in the sky and shines more brightly.

10 National Explosive Ordnance Disposal (EOD) Day is held on the first Saturday of May every year. It was created to recognize and honor the professionals who disarm and dispose of explosives, nuclear, biological, and chemical weapons.

11 The Moon's orbit around the Earth (synodic period) takes 29.530587 days.

12 The Witch's Ladder is a bit of very old folk magic. It was brought to popular attention through an article in *Folk-Lore Journal in 1887. Later,* Charles Godfrey Leland (author of Aradia: Gospel of the Witches) wrote extensively about his investigations into the "witches garland" or "rope and feathers".

13 *Equinox* is Latin for *equal night. Equilux* is Latin for *equal light.* On the Equinoxes, the equator is the closest point of the Earth to the Sun. Almost every Witchcraft book will tell you that the Equinox Sabbats are times when day and night are equal, but that isn't entirely correct. More accurately it should be stated that the Equinox Sabbat is when day and night are *almost equal*. Due to light refraction on the horizon, the actual time of equal day and night is Equilux, which usually comes a few days before the actual Vernal Equinox and a few days after the exact Autumnal Equinox.

14 For the sake of this example I've set ethical considerations aside. For Witches who practice the Wiccan Rede, some reflection on the intent and ramifications of this type of spell may be necessary.

15 Illustration of European Mandrake was adopted from the book *Stirpium historiae pemptades sex sive libri XXX* by Flemish botanist and physician Rembert Dodoens.

16 There has been an obvious lack of words for modern forms of divination. Shufflemancy is one of the more recent terms used but is specific to music listened to on various media players. I've created Mediaomancy as an overall grouping of these increasingly popular methods.

17 Moon day is in recognition of the Lunar Module landing on July 20, 1969. When it touched down on the moon at Tranquility Base, Apollo 11 Commander Neil Armstrong reported "The Eagle Has Landed". The Module's was named the "Eagle". A few hours later, Neil Armstrong, stepped off of the Eagle's ladder, placed one foot upon the moon's surface and proclaimed: "That's one small step for a man, one giant leap for mankind".